Discovering
Advanced
Algebra
An Investigative Approach

More Practice Your Skills
with Answers

DISCOVERING

MATHEMATICS™

Key Curriculum Press
Innovators in Mathematics Education

Teacher's Materials Project Editor: Joan Lewis

Project Editor: Heather Dever

Editorial Assistants: Erin Gray, Eric Martin

Writer: Abby Tanenbaum

Accuracy Checker: Karen Douglass

Production Editors: Angela Chen, Stephanie Tanaka

Copyeditor: Margaret Moore

Editorial Production Manager: Deborah Cogan

Production Director: Diana Jean Ray

Production Coordinator: Ann Rothenbuhler

Text Designer: Jenny Somerville

Art Editor: Jason Luz

Composition, Technical Art: Interactive Composition Corporation

Art and Design Coordinator: Marilyn Perry

Cover Designer: Jill Kongabel

Printer: Von Hoffmann Corporation

Executive Editor: Casey FitzSimons

Publisher: Steven Rasmussen

Cover Photo Credits: Background and center images: NASA; all other images: Ken Karp Photography.

Key Curriculum Press
1150 65th Street
Emeryville, CA 94608
(510) 595-7000
editorial@keypress.com
www.keypress.com

Printed in the United States of America
10 9 8 7 6 5 4 3 2 1   07 06 05 04 03   ISBN 1-55953-613-6

Contents

Chapter 9

Chapter 10

Chapter 11

Chapter 12

Chapter 13

Introduction

The authors of *Discovering Advanced Algebra: An Investigative Approach* are aware of the importance of students developing algebra skills along with acquiring concepts through investigation. The student book includes many skill-based exercises. These *More Practice Your Skills* worksheets provide problems similar to the Practice Your Skills exercises in *Discovering Advanced Algebra*. Like the Practice Your Skills exercises, these worksheets allow students to practice and reinforce the important procedures and skills developed in the lessons. Some of these problems provide non-contextual skills practice. Others give students an opportunity to apply skills in fairly simple, straightforward contexts. Some are more complex problems that are broken down into small steps. And some have several parts, each giving practice with the same skill.

You might assign the *More Practice Your Skills* worksheet for every lesson, or only for those lessons your students find particularly difficult. Or you may wish to assign the worksheets on an individual basis, only to those students who need extra help. One worksheet has been provided for every lesson. The worksheets for Chapter 0 provide a review of beginning algebra skills. To save you the time and expense of copying pages, you can give students the inexpensive *More Practice Your Skills Student Workbook,* which does not have answers. Though the limited reproduction permission allows you to copy pages from *More Practice Your Skills with Answers* for use with your students, the consumable *More Practice Your Skills Student Workbook* should not be copied. You can also use the *Discovering Advanced Algebra Test Generator and Worksheet Builder*™ CD to generate additional practice sheets for students who need further practice.

Lesson 0.1 • Pictures, Graphs, and Diagrams

Name _____ Period _____ Date _____

1. Find the slope of each line.

a.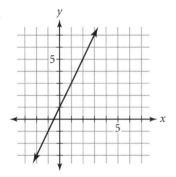

b.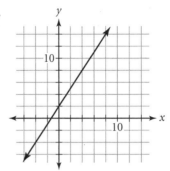

c.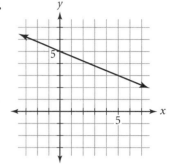

2. Solve.

a. $\dfrac{4}{7} = \dfrac{a}{21}$

b. $\dfrac{5}{9} = \dfrac{20}{b}$

c. $\dfrac{c}{42} = \dfrac{11}{14}$

d. $\dfrac{54}{d} = \dfrac{9}{13}$

e. $\dfrac{w}{8} = \dfrac{81}{72}$

f. $\dfrac{3}{14} = \dfrac{60}{x}$

g. $\dfrac{52}{y} = \dfrac{13}{18}$

h. $\dfrac{21}{36} = \dfrac{z}{24}$

i. $\dfrac{49}{q} = \dfrac{7}{10}$

3. Find the slope of the line that passes through each pair of points.

a. $(0, 1)$ and $(3, 8)$

b. $(3, 5)$ and $(5, 0)$

c. $(-2, 3)$ and $(4, 9)$

d. $(-8, 0)$ and $(0, -8)$

e. $(-5, -2)$ and $(-8, 4)$

f. $(-1, 7)$ and $(-5, 2)$

g. $(-10, -8)$ and $(-20, 22)$

h. $(6, 6)$ and $(-1, -5)$

4. Convert each fraction to decimal form.

a. $\dfrac{5}{16}$

b. $\dfrac{7}{25}$

c. $\dfrac{4}{9}$

d. $\dfrac{8}{11}$

e. $\dfrac{3}{7}$

f. $\dfrac{11}{12}$

g. $\dfrac{27}{40}$

h. $\dfrac{74}{75}$

i. $\dfrac{15}{11}$

5. Convert each decimal value to fraction form. Write all fractions in lowest terms.

a. 0.875

b. 1.3

c. $0.\overline{5}$

d. $0.41\overline{6}$

e. 1.75

f. $0.\overline{18}$

g. 0.9375

h. $0.\overline{47}$

i. $0.\overline{63}$

Lesson 0.2 • Symbolic Representation

Name _____ Period _____ Date _____

1. Explain what you would do to change the first equation to the second.

    a. $x + 7 = 22$
          $x = 15$

    b. $8y = 72$
          $y = 9$

    c. $-14 + z = 21$
           $z = 35$

    d. $\dfrac{w}{-11} = 2.5$
         $w = -27.5$

    e. $280 = r + 116$
         $164 = r$

    f. $323 = -19s$
         $-17 = s$

2. Solve.

    a. $12 + a = 39$
    b. $42 - b = 33$

    c. $25c = 375$
    d. $5 + 3d = -7$

    e. $x + 4x = 35$
    f. $2y + 3y = -130$

    g. $6z + z + 8 = -20$
    h. $12 + 9w = w - 15$

    i. $-14 + 3p = -9p - 21$
    j. $15 - 6q = 2q + 9$

3. Rewrite each expression without parentheses.

    a. $5(x - 9)$
    b. $-3(7 - y)$

    c. $2z(z - 8)$
    d. $-12q(12 - q)$

    e. $-7y(y^2 - 3y)$
    f. $10x(x^2 - 10)$

    g. $(2r - 5)(3r)$
    h. $(-8s + 5)(-6s)$

    i. $-y^2(3y - 5)$
    j. $8z(2z^2 - 15)$

4. Substitute the given value of the variable(s) in each expression and evaluate.

    a. $4x - 12$ when $x = 3$

    b. $5(y + 7)$ when $y = -12$

    c. $-2a + 5b$ when $a = -3$ and $b = 6$

    d. $\frac{1}{2}m - \frac{3}{4}n$ when $m = -8$ and $n = -12$

    e. $0.2a - 0.4b + 0.6c$ when $a = 20$, $b = -32$, and $c = 16$

    f. $\frac{5}{6}x + \frac{2}{3}y - \frac{7}{12}z$ when $x = -12$, $y = 9$, and $z = 24$

    g. $2.3r - 4.5s - 5.8t$ when $r = 4$, $s = -2$, and $t = -5$

    h. $\frac{3}{8}f - \frac{5}{11}h + \frac{9}{7}j$ when $f = -8$, $h = -22$, and $j = 21$

Discovering Advanced Algebra More Practice Your Skills
©2004 Key Curriculum Press

Lesson 0.3 • Organizing Information

Name _____ Period _____ Date _____

1. Use the distributive property to expand each expression, and combine like terms when possible.

   a. $2.6(w - 4)$

   b. $8 - 3.5(x - 6)$

   c. $4.3 - (2y + 8.9)$

   d. $3.1(12 - z) - 15.9$

   e. $-5(7.5r + 3.7)$

   f. $6.8s - 2.8(t - 3)$

   g. $-2(6u + 8) + 5(3u - 2)$

   h. $8(7v - 5) - 9(6v - 4)$

   i. $\frac{1}{2}(8v - 6) + \frac{2}{3}(15v - 9)$

   j. $\frac{8}{11}(22z + 33) - \frac{12}{13}(26z + 13)$

2. Solve.

   a. $6(p - 9) = -33$

   b. $-8(q + 12) = 10.4$

   c. $2.5(t - 1.6) = 8$

   d. $-9.8(u + 1.5) = -181.3$

   e. $2.5(m - 8) = 12.5$

   f. $-4.8(n + 3) = 19.2$

   g. $1.9(r - 9) - 16 = 4.9$

   h. $22 - 5(s + 6) = 32$

   i. $4.5(z + 6) + 24.5 = -7$

   j. $1.5(22 - w) + 13 = 2w - 69.5$

3. Rewrite each expression using the properties of exponents so that the variable appears only once.

   a. $\left(m^4\right)\left(m^8\right)$

   b. $\left(n^9\right)\left(n^{11}\right)$

   c. $t\left(t^{20}\right)$

   d. $\frac{r^{13}}{r^8}$

   e. $\frac{\left(s^{15}\right)\left(s^{18}\right)}{s^{30}}$

   f. $\frac{\left(p^{13}\right)(p)}{p^{24}}$

   g. $\left(v^5\right)^3$

   h. $\left(w^{10}\right)^{10}$

   i. $\left(2x^4\right)^3$

   j. $\left(-y^2z^3\right)^6$

   k. $\left(-3a^2b\right)^4$

   l. $\frac{\left(4x^6\right)(-5x)^2}{(10x)\left(-x^2\right)^3}$

4. Expand each product and combine like terms.

   a. $(x + 4)(x + 5)$

   b. $(y - 3)(y - 7)$

   c. $(z - 7)(z + 2)$

   d. $(r - 12)(r + 15)$

   e. $(s + 11)(s - 11)$

   f. $(t + 4)^2$

   g. $(v - 7)^2$

   h. $(2m - 3)^2$

   i. $(5n + 1)^2$

   j. $(7p - 9)(7p + 9)$

   k. $(5y + 1)(2y + 7)$

   l. $(2x - 5)(3x + 4)$

Lesson 1.1 • Recursively Defined Sequences

Name _____ Period _____ Date _____

1. Tell whether each sequence is arithmetic, geometric, or neither.

   a. $1, 5, 9, 13, \ldots$
   b. $2, 6, 18, 54, \ldots$
   c. $1, 1, 2, 3, 5, 8, \ldots$
   d. $16, 4, 1, 0.25, \ldots$
   e. $-1, 1, -1, 1, \ldots$
   f. $5.6, 2.8, 0, -2.8, \ldots$

2. Find the common difference, d, for each arithmetic sequence and the common ratio, r, for each geometric sequence.

   a. $6, 11, 16, 21, \ldots$
   b. $100, 10, 1, 0.1, \ldots$
   c. $1.5, 1.0, 0.5, 0, -0.5, \ldots$
   d. $0.0625, 0.125, 0.25, \ldots$
   e. $-1, 0.2, -0.04, 0.008, \ldots$
   f. $-4, -3.99, -3.98, \ldots$

3. Write the first six terms of each sequence, starting with u_1.

   a. $u_1 = -18$
   $u_n = u_{n-1} + 6$ where $n \geq 2$

   b. $u_1 = 0.5$
   $u_n = 3u_{n-1}$ where $n \geq 2$

   c. $u_1 = 35.6$
   $u_n = u_{n-1} - 4.2$ where $n \geq 2$

   d. $u_1 = 8$
   $u_n = -\dfrac{1}{2}u_{n-1}$ where $n \geq 2$

4. Write a recursive formula to generate each sequence. Then find the indicated term.

   a. $-15, -11, -7, -3, \ldots$ Find the 10th term.

   b. $1000, 100, 10, 1, \ldots$ Find the 12th term.

   c. $17.25, 14.94, 12.63, 10.32, \ldots$ Find the 15th term.

   d. $0.3, -0.03, 0.003, -0.0003, \ldots$ Find the 8th term.

   e. $0, \dfrac{1}{6}, \dfrac{1}{3}, \dfrac{1}{2}, \ldots$ Find the 21st term.

   f. $-2, 4, -8, 16, \ldots$ Find the 15th term.

5. Indicate whether each situation could be represented by an arithmetic sequence or a geometric sequence. Give the value of the common difference, d, for each arithmetic sequence and of the common ratio, r, for each geometric sequence.

   a. Phil rented an apartment for $850 a month. Each time he renewed his lease over the next 3 years, his landlord raised the rent by $50.

   b. Leora was hired as a first-year teacher at an annual salary of $30,000. She received an annual salary increase of 5% for each of the next 4 years.

   c. A laboratory technician observes that the number of bacteria in a colony doubles every 12 hours.

   d. The number of students enrolled in a high school is decreasing at a rate of 75 students per year.

6. Write a recursive formula for the sequence graphed at right. Find the 42nd term.

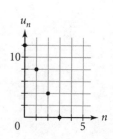

Lesson 1.2 • Modeling Growth and Decay

Name _____ Period _____ Date _____

1. Find the common ratio for each sequence.

   a. 42, 126, 378, 1134, . . .

   b. 19.2, 3.84, 0.768, 0.1536, . . .

   c. 90, 99, 108.9, 119.79, . . .

   d. 1800, 1080, 648, 388.8, . . .

   e. 11.5, 43.7, 166.06, 631.028, . . .

   f. 375, 142.5, 54.15, 20.577, . . .

2. Identify each sequence in Exercise 1 as growth or decay and give the percent increase or decrease for each.

3. Write a recursive formula for each sequence in Exercise 1 and find the 6th term. Use u_1 for the first term given.

4. Factor each expression so that the variable appears only once.

   a. $x + 0.25x$

   b. $y - 0.19y$

   c. $2A - 0.33A$

   d. $3B + 0.07B$

   e. $u_{n-1} + 0.085u_{n-1}$

   f. $u_{n-1} - 0.72u_{n-1}$

   g. $3u_{n-1} - 0.5u_{n-1}$

   h. $1.5u_{n-1} + 0.25u_{n-1}$

5. Find the percent increase or percent decrease in each situation. (Round to the nearest tenth of a percent.) Identify each change as an increase or a decrease.

   a. The number of students attending a high school grew from 1260 to 1580.

   b. A computer originally priced at $2100 was put on sale for $1850.

   c. When Melissa renewed her lease, her rent went up from $780 to $815.

   d. After laying off 560 employees, a company had 1266 employees left.

   e. The value of a car depreciated from $15,900 to $12,402.

   f. The population of a small town changed from 16,350 to 17,331.

6. Match each recursive formula to a graph.

   a. $u_1 = 35$
      $u_n = (1 - 0.3) \cdot u_{n-1}$ where $n \geq 2$

   b. $u_1 = 35$
      $u_n = (1 - 0.5) \cdot u_{n-1}$ where $n \geq 2$

   c. $u_1 = 35$
      $u_n = -0.5 + u_{n-1}$ where $n \geq 2$

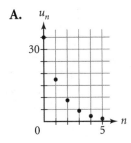

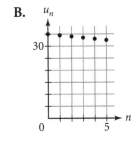

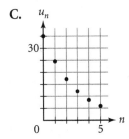

Lesson 1.3 • A First Look at Limits

Name _____ Period _____ Date _____

1. For each sequence, find the value of u_1, u_2, and u_3. Identify the type of sequence (arithmetic, geometric, or shifted geometric) and tell whether it is increasing or decreasing.

a. $u_0 = 25$
   $u_n = u_{n-1} + 8$ where $n \geq 1$

b. $u_0 = 10$
   $u_n = 0.1u_{n-1}$ where $n \geq 1$

c. $u_0 = 48$
   $u_n = u_{n-1} - 6.9$ where $n \geq 1$

d. $u_0 = 100$
   $u_n = 1.01u_{n-1}$ where $n \geq 1$

e. $u_0 = 500$
   $u_n = (1 - 0.80)u_{n-1} + 25$ where $n \geq 1$

f. $u_0 = 490$
   $u_n = (1 + 0.70)u_{n-1} - 50$ where $n \geq 1$

2. Solve.

a. $r = 0.9r + 30$

b. $s = 25 + 0.75s$

c. $t = 0.82t$

d. $v = 45 + v$

e. $w = 0.60w - 20$

f. $z = 0.125z + 49$

3. Find the long-run value for each sequence.

a. $u_0 = 25$
   $u_n = 0.8u_{n-1}$ where $n \geq 1$

b. $u_0 = 100$
   $u_n = 0.1u_{n-1}$ where $n \geq 1$

c. $u_0 = 48$
   $u_n = 0.75u_{n-1} + 25$ where $n \geq 1$

d. $u_0 = 12$
   $u_n = 0.9u_{n-1} + 2$ where $n \geq 1$

e. $u_0 = 62$
   $u_n = (1 - 0.2)u_{n-1}$ where $n \geq 1$

f. $u_0 = 45$
   $u_n = (1 - 0.05)u_{n-1} + 5$ where $n \geq 1$

g. $u_0 = 500$
   $u_n = (1 - 0.80)u_{n-1} + 25$ where $n \geq 1$

h. $u_0 = 350$
   $u_n = (1 - 0.75)u_{n-1} - 30$ where $n \geq 1$

4. Write a recursive formula for each sequence. Use u_0 for the first term given.

a. 0, 20, 36, 48.8, . . .

b. 100, 160, 226, 298.6, . . .

c. 50, 36, 27.6, 22.56, . . .

d. 40, 44, 50.4, 60.64, . . .

e. 180, 144, 111.6, 82.44, . . .

f. 2500, 1280, 670, 365, . . .

g. 500, 650, 830, 1046, . . .

h. 90, 67, 48.6, 33.88, . . .

Discovering Advanced Algebra More Practice Your Skills
©2004 Key Curriculum Press

Lesson 1.4 • Graphing Sequences

Name _____ Period _____ Date _____

1. Write five ordered pairs that represent points on the graph of each sequence.

   a. $u_0 = 2$
      $u_n = u_{n-1} + 8$ where $n \geq 1$

   b. $u_0 = 10$
      $u_n = 0.1u_{n-1}$ where $n \geq 1$

   c. $u_0 = 0$
      $u_n = 2.5u_{n-1} + 10$ where $n \geq 1$

   d. $u_0 = 150$
      $u_n = 0.8u_{n-1} - 10$ where $n \geq 1$

   e. $u_0 = 60$
      $u_n = 0.75u_{n-1} + 15$ where $n \geq 1$

   f. $u_0 = 250$
      $u_n = 1.2u_{n-1} - 25$ where $n \geq 1$

2. Identify each graph as a representation of an arithmetic sequence, a geometric sequence, or a shifted geometric sequence. Use an informed guess to write a recursive rule for each.

   a.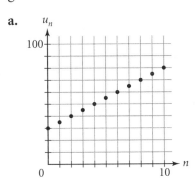

   b.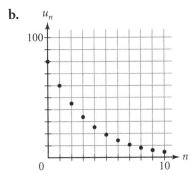

   c.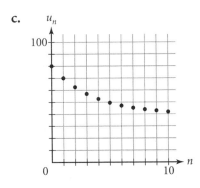

   d.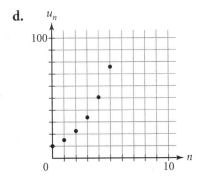

3. Imagine the graphs of the sequences generated by these recursive formulas. Describe each graph using exactly three of these terms: arithmetic, geometric, shifted geometric, linear, nonlinear, increasing, decreasing.

   a. $u_0 = 50$
      $u_n = u_{n-1} - 10$ where $n \geq 1$

   b. $u_0 = 1000$
      $u_n = 0.7u_{n-1} + 100$ where $n \geq 1$

   c. $u_0 = 35$
      $u_n = u_{n-1} \cdot 1.75$ where $n \geq 1$

   d. $u_0 = 150$
      $u_n = (1 - 0.15)u_{n-1}$ where $n \geq 1$

   e. $u_0 = 5.0$
      $u_n = 0.1 + u_{n-1}$ where $n \geq 1$

   f. $u_0 = 88$
      $u_n = (1 + 0.3)u_{n-1} - 10$ where $n \geq 1$

Lesson 1.5 • Loans and Investments

Name _____ Period _____ Date _____

1. Assume that each of the sequences below represents a financial situation. Indicate whether each represents a loan or an investment, and give the principal and the deposit or payment amount.

   a. $u_0 = 1000$

   $u_n = (1 + 0.04)u_{n-1} + 100$ where $n \geq 1$

   b. $u_0 = 15500$

   $u_n = \left(1 + \dfrac{0.06}{2}\right)u_{n-1} - 475$ where $n \geq 1$

   c. $u_0 = 130000$

   $u_n = \left(1 + \dfrac{0.0625}{4}\right)u_{n-1} - 1055$ where $n \geq 1$

   d. $u_0 = 1825$

   $u_n = \left(1 + \dfrac{0.075}{12}\right)u_{n-1} + 120$ where $n \geq 11$

2. For each financial situation represented by a sequence in Exercise 1, give the annual interest rate and the frequency with which interest is compounded.

3. Find the first month's interest on each loan.

   a. $20,000 loan; 6% annual interest rate

   b. $1,650 loan; 4.6% annual interest rate

   c. $122,750 loan; 5.75% annual interest rate

   d. $49,200 loan; 7.3% annual interest rate

4. Write a recursive formula for each financial situation.

   a. You invest $5,000 at 5%, compounded quarterly, and deposit an additional $400 every 3 months.

   b. You take out a car loan for $12,500 at 7.5%, compounded monthly, and you make monthly payments of $350.

   c. You take out a home mortgage for $144,500 at 6.2%, compounded monthly, and make monthly payments of $990.

   d. You enroll in an investment plan through your job that deducts $225 from your monthly paycheck and deposits it into an account with an annual interest rate of 3.75%, compounded monthly.

Discovering Advanced Algebra More Practice Your Skills
©2004 Key Curriculum Press

Lesson 2.1 • Measures of Central Tendency and Box Plots

Name _____ Period _____ Date _____

1. Find the mean, median, and mode for each data set.

    a. {2, 3, 5, 5, 7, 7, 7, 8, 9, 10}

    b. {8, 7, 5, 6, 3, 2, 9, 8}

    c. {210, 180, 188, 162, 170}

    d. {4.5, 20.7, 35.2, 28.8, 36.5, 40.5}

    e. {5.3, 8.4, 5.3, 9.2, 10.6, 9.2}

    f. {2150, 1860, 2340, 1990}

2. Invent a data set that matches each description.

    a. Five values, *mean* = 15, *median* = 13, no mode

    b. Six values, *mean* = 24, *median* = 25, *mode* = 28

3. Suppose that you have a data set containing 1000 test scores. How many scores would you expect to find matching each description?

    a. Above the median

    b. Below the first quartile

    c. Between the first and third quartiles

    d. Above the third quartile

    e. Below the third quartile

    f. Above the first quartile

    g. Between the median and the third quartile

4. Give the five-number summary for each data set.

    a. {10, 8, 6, 4, 2}

    b. {0, 30, 45, 50, 75, 80, 95}

    c. {8, 6, 8, 2, 9, 4, 4, 3, 1}

    d. {32, 55, 16, 70, 65, 55, 40, 49}

    e. {19.3, 32.4, 20.5, 18.0, 26.6, 21.4, 16.7, 33.9}

    f. {0.52, 3.91, 4.67, 2.20, 8.15, 5.91, 7.94, 1.11, 6.55, 4.03}

5. Match each box plot to one of the data sets below.

    a.
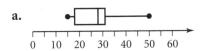

    b.
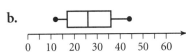

    A. {29, 16, 20, 28, 5, 50, 15}

    B. {30, 18, 22, 28, 31, 15, 50}

    C. {21, 12, 33, 44, 26, 15, 36}

    D. {48, 41, 35, 12, 15, 19, 26}

Lesson 2.2 • Measures of Spread

Name _____ **Period** _____ **Date** _____

1. For each data set, find the mean, the deviation from the mean for each value, and the standard deviation of the data set. (Round to the nearest tenth.)

   a. {12.4, 26.3, 9.8, 33.9, 7.6}   b. {235, 413, 505, 111, 700, 626, 357}

   c. {0.5, 2.6, 1.8, 4.7, 0.9}

2. For each data set, give the mean and the standard deviation. Include appropriate units in your answers.

   a. The heights in inches of eight children are 32, 45, 39, 51, 28, 54, 37, and 42.

   b. The lengths in centimeters of six pencils are 8.5, 19.0, 11.8, 13.2, 16.4, and 6.1.

   c. The prices of seven music CDs are $13.50, $10.95, $9.95, $16.00, $12.50, $15.95, and $17.75.

3. For each data set, find the median, the range, and the *IQR*.

   a. {18, 13, 15, 24, 20}   b. {4, 9, 7, 6, 0, 11, 7}

   c. {356, 211, 867, 779, 101, 543}

4. Identify all outliers in each data set.

   a. {20, 8, 32, 18, 105, 4, 45}   b. {3.2, 4.9, 1.6, 2.8, 5.5}

   c. {35, 38, 5, 46, 49, 41, 52, 95}

Discovering Advanced Algebra More Practice Your Skills
©2004 Key Curriculum Press

Lesson 2.3 • Histograms and Percentile Ranks

Name _____ Period _____ Date _____

1. The following data represent the ages of family members attending a family reunion.

   {9, 5, 25, 29, 40, 48, 63, 56, 3, 32, 38, 53, 79, 0, 85, 87, 12, 14, 32, 5, 54, 67, 78, 75}

   Draw a histogram for these data with the given number of bins.

   a. 9   **b.** 6

2. For each of the following histograms, give the bin width and the number of values in the data set. Then identify the bin that contains the median of the data.

   a.
   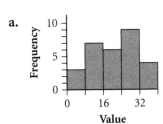

   b.
   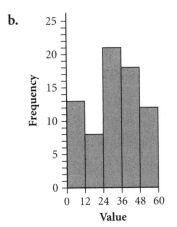

   c.
   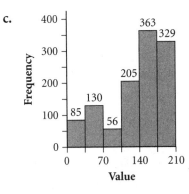

3. Find each percentile rank.

   a. 73 out of 100 employees in a company earn less than $45,000 a year. Find the percentile rank of an employee who earns $45,000 a year.

   b. 460 out of 1000 students scored at least 30 points out of 50 on a standardized test. Find the percentile rank of a student who scored 30 points on the test.

   c. 220 out of 500 families spend less than $50 per month on long-distance telephone calls. Find the percentile rank of a family that spends $50 per month on long-distance calls.

   d. 76 out of 200 people living alone spend $650 a month or more on rent. Find the percentile rank of a person who spends $650 a month on rent.

Lesson 3.1 • Linear Equations and Arithmetic Sequences

Name _____ Period _____ Date _____

1. Find an explicit formula for each recursively defined arithmetic sequence.

   a. $u_0 = 5$
   $u_n = u_{n-1} + 8$ where $n \geq 1$

   b. $u_0 = 4.5$
   $u_n = u_{n-1} + 3.2$ where $n \geq 1$

   c. $u_0 = 18.25$
   $u_n = u_{n-1} - 4.75$ where $n \geq 1$

   d. $u_0 = 0$
   $u_n = u_{n-1} + 100$ where $n \geq 1$

2. Refer to the graph of the sequence.

   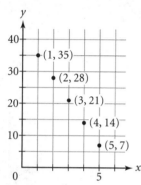

   a. Write a recursive formula for the sequence. What is the common difference? What is the value of u_0?

   b. What is the slope of the line through the points? What is the y-intercept?

   c. Write the equation of the line that contains these points.

3. For each sequence, find n so that u_n has the specified value.

   a. $u_n = 4 + 5n$
   $u_n = 79$

   b. $u_0 = 88$
   $u_n = u_{n-1} - 7.5$ where $n \geq 1$
   $u_n = -84.5$

4. Find the slope of each line.

   a. $y = 5 + 3x$

   b. $y = 10 - x$

   c. $y = 0.6x - 0.8$

   d. $y = \dfrac{2}{5} - \dfrac{4}{5}x$

   e. $y = 12.5$

   f. $y = 7 + x$

5. Write an equation in the form $y = a + bx$ for each line.

   a. The line that passes through the points of an arithmetic sequence with $u_0 = 11$ and a common difference of 9

   b. The line that passes through the points of an arithmetic sequence with $u_0 = -7.5$ and a common difference of -12.5

Discovering Advanced Algebra More Practice Your Skills
©2004 Key Curriculum Press

Lesson 3.2 • Revisiting Slope

Name _____ Period _____ Date _____

1. Find the slope of the line containing each pair of points.

   a. $(2, 6)$ and $(4, 12)$ **b.** $(-5, 2)$ and $(2, -5)$ **c.** $(0, 7)$ and $(5, 0)$

   d. $\left(\frac{1}{3}, \frac{2}{3}\right)$ and $\left(\frac{5}{6}, -\frac{1}{6}\right)$ **e.** $(8, 12)$ and $(-3, 12)$ **f.** $(-9, 8)$ and $(-9, -8)$

2. Find the slope of each line.

   a. $y = 4x - 5$ **b.** $y = 1.6 - 2.5x$ **c.** $7x - 6y = 42$

   d. $3x + 5y = 15$ **e.** $y = -4(x - 7) + 12$ **f.** $y = 14.5 - 0.3(x - 30)$

3. Solve.

   a. $y = 6 - 2x$ for y if $x = -4$.

   b. $y = 32 + 5x$ for x if $y = 8$.

   c. $y = a - 0.4x$ for a if $x = 600$ and $y = 150$.

   d. $y = 375 + bx$ for b if $x = 20$ and $y = 500$.

4. Find the equations of both lines in each graph.

   a. 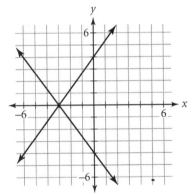   **b.**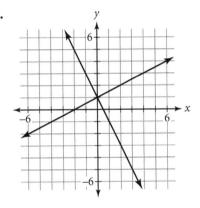

5. Consider the equations and graphs of Exercise 4.

   a. What do the equations in 4a have in common? What do you notice about their graphs?

   b. What do the equations in 4b have in common? What do you notice about their graphs?

Lesson 3.3 • Fitting a Line to Data

Name _____ Period _____ Date _____

1. Write an equation in point-slope form for each line.

   a.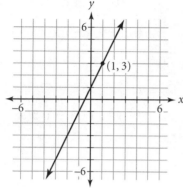

   b.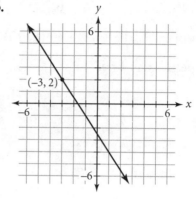

2. Write an equation in point-slope form for each line.

   a. Slope -3 and passing through $(2, 5)$

   b. Slope 0.75 and passing through $(-4, 10)$

   c. Parallel to $y = 5 + 3x$ and passing through $(-4, 2)$

   d. Parallel to $y = 7 - 4x$ and passing through $(2, -5)$

3. Solve.

   a. $u_n = 8 + 6(n - 2)$ for u_n if $n = 10$.

   b. $d = 9 - 4(t + 5)$ for d if $t = 20$.

   c. $y = 500 - 20(x - 5)$ for x if $y = 240$.

   d. $u_n = -3.5 + 0.4(n - 12)$ for n if $u_n = 2.9$.

4. For each graph, use your ruler to draw a line of fit. Explain how your line satisfies the guidelines on page 128 of your book.

   a.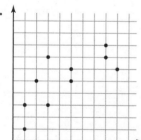

   b.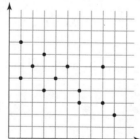

Discovering Advanced Algebra More Practice Your Skills
©2004 Key Curriculum Press

Lesson 3.4 • The Median-Median Line

Name _____ Period _____ Date _____

1. How should you divide the following sets into three groups for the median-median line?

   a. Set of 33 elements

   b. Set of 44 elements

   c. Set of 64 elements

   d. Set of 57 elements

2. Find the point with coordinates (*median x, median y*) for each group of points.

   a. $(3, 4), (5, 8), (11, 9), (13, 10)$

   b. $(0, 3), (2, 6), (3, 4), (5, 1), (7, 5)$

   c. $(14, 20), (11, 11), (17, 13), (15, 19), (16, 22), (20, 18)$

   d. $(2.5, 5.0), (4.1, 3.8), (1.6, 7.5), (5.9, 2.6)$

3. Find an equation in point-slope form for the line passing through each pair of points.

   a. $(5, 8)$ and $(8, 2)$

   b. $(-1, 6)$ and $(9, -4)$

   c. $(20, -14)$ and $(-30, 16)$

   d. $(44.2, -22.8)$ and $(25.2, 34.2)$

4. Find an equation for each line described. Write your answer in the same form as the given line or lines.

   a. Line one-third of the way from $y = 2x + 6$ to $y = 2x + 15$

   b. Line one-third of the way from $y = 5 - x$ to $y = 11 - x$

   c. Line one-third of the way from $y = 16.4 + 3.8x$ to the point $(9, 50)$

   d. Line one-third of the way from $y = 0.8x + 12.6$ to the point $(9, 48)$

Lesson 3.5 • Residuals

Name _____ Period _____ Date _____

1. Determine whether the given point lies above or below the given line.

   a. $y = 4x + 5$; $(1, 8)$

   b. $y = -2x + 6$; $(3, 1)$

   c. $y = 3.6x - 18.8$; $(10, 16.9)$

   d. $y = -0.1x + 4.4$; $(5, 4.2)$

2. Each of the equations below represents the median-median line for a set of data. The table gives the x-value and the residual for each data point. Find the y-value for each data point.

   a. $\hat{y} = 4x - 5$

x-value	0	1	3	10
Residual	1	−1	2	−3

   b. $\hat{y} = 3.2x + 6.7$

x-value	3	5	10	22
Residual	−1.3	2.3	0.3	−3.1

3. This table gives the number of students enrolled in U.S. public schools for various years.

   a. Find the median-median line for the data. Round all answers to one decimal place. Does the y-intercept make sense for the data?

   b. Calculate the residuals.

   c. Calculate the root mean square error for the median-median line.

   d. What is the real-world meaning of the root mean square error?

   e. The *World Almanac* predicts that the public school enrollment in the 2009–10 school year will be 47,109 students. Use your median-median line to predict enrollment in 2009–10 and calculate the residual of the *Almanac's* prediction.

School year	Public school enrollment
1909–10	17,814
1919–20	21,578
1929–30	25,678
1939–40	25,434
1949–50	25,111
1959–60	35,182
1969–70	45,550
1979–80	41,651
1989–90	40,543
1999–2000	46,812

   (*The World Almanac and Book of Facts 2001*)

4. Each list of numbers below represents the residuals for a data set. Find the root mean square error for each set of residuals. (Round your answers to the nearest hundredth.)

   a. $3, -2, 1, 0, -3, -2, 4$

   b. $5, -3, -4, 6, 1, 2, -2$

Discovering Advanced Algebra More Practice Your Skills
©2004 Key Curriculum Press

Lesson 3.6 • Linear Systems

Name _____ Period _____ Date _____

1. Identify the point of intersection listed below each system of linear equations that is the solution of that system.

   a. $\begin{cases} 2x + 5y = 10 \\ x - 3y = -6 \end{cases}$
   $(5, 0); (0, 2); (3, 1)$

   b. $\begin{cases} 4x + 3y = 4 \\ 3x - 2y = -14 \end{cases}$
   $(-2, 4); \left(0, \dfrac{4}{3}\right); (0, 7)$

   c. $\begin{cases} 6x - 5y = 0 \\ x - y = -1 \end{cases}$
   $(0, 0); (-5, -6); (5, 6)$

2. Write a system of linear equations that has each ordered pair as its solution.

   a. $(5, 4)$

   b. $(-3, 8)$

   c. $(3, 10.5)$

3. Write an equation for each line described.

   a. Perpendicular to $y = 2x - 3$ and passing through the point $(5, -4)$

   b. Perpendicular to $y = 1.5 + 0.25x$ and passing through the point $(5, -2)$

4. Solve.

   a. $8 - 3(x - 2) = 5 + 6x$

   b. $120 - 5.5(x - 45) = 75 - x$

   c. $3.8t - 16.2 = 12 + 2.8(t + 3)$

   d. $7.5 - 0.8t = 18.5 + 3.2(t - 4)$

5. Use substitution to find the point (x, y) where each pair of lines intersect. Use a graph or table to verify your answer.

   a. $\begin{cases} y = 3 - 2x \\ y = 5 + 2x \end{cases}$

   b. $\begin{cases} y = -2.5x + 8 \\ y = 1.5x - 4 \end{cases}$

   c. $\begin{cases} y = 0.45x - 2 \\ y = -0.45x + 2 \end{cases}$

   d. $\begin{cases} y = 9 + 4(x - 3) \\ y = 15 - 2x \end{cases}$

   e. $\begin{cases} y = -2x + 7.5 \\ y = 3x - 15 \end{cases}$

   f. $\begin{cases} y = 4.8 - 2(x + 3.1) \\ y = 13.6 + 3x \end{cases}$

Lesson 3.7 • Substitution and Elimination

Name _____   Period _____   Date _____

1. Solve for the given variable.

   a. $r - s = 20$, for s

   c. $3x + 4y = 12$, for y

   e. $0.2m - 0.5n = 1$, for n

   b. $2w + z = 8$, for w

   d. $5x - 8y = -10$, for x

   f. $250x + 400y = -50$, for y

2. Find a multiplier for the first equation so that the sum of the resulting new equation and the second original equation will eliminate y. (Do not solve the system.)

   a. $\begin{cases} 4x - 5y = 2 \\ x + 10y = -2 \end{cases}$

   b. $\begin{cases} 5.5x + 2.5y = 4 \\ 2.0x + 7.5y = -1 \end{cases}$

   c. $\begin{cases} 1.6x - 3.2y = 0 \\ 5x + 16y = 8 \end{cases}$

3. Graph each system and find an approximate solution. Then choose a method and find the exact solution. List each solution as an ordered pair.

   a. $\begin{cases} x + y = 1 \\ 2x - 2y = 1 \end{cases}$

   b. $\begin{cases} 3x - 2y = 6 \\ -2x + 3y = 0 \end{cases}$

   c. $\begin{cases} 5x + 4y = 16 \\ 4x - 3y = 12 \end{cases}$

4. Solve each system of equations.

   a. $\begin{cases} 3x - 4y = 8 \\ y = x - 1 \end{cases}$

   b. $\begin{cases} 2x + 3y = 0 \\ 3x + 2y = -10 \end{cases}$

   c. $\begin{cases} 5x - 8y = 8 \\ -10x + 4y = -7 \end{cases}$

   d. $\begin{cases} 0.5x + 1.5y = 5 \\ x + y = -10 \end{cases}$

   e. $\begin{cases} -4x + 15y = 8 \\ 6x - 5y = -5 \end{cases}$

   f. $\begin{cases} 5x - 9y = 8.5 \\ 3x + 7y = -1.1 \end{cases}$

   g. $\begin{cases} 0.3x + 0.8y = 3.6 \\ 0.7x + 0.3y = -5.7 \end{cases}$

   h. $\begin{cases} 0.9x - 0.4y = 21 \\ 0.2x + 0.6y = -16 \end{cases}$

   i. $\begin{cases} 0.6x + 0.5y = 6.4 \\ 1.4x - 0.7y = -44.8 \end{cases}$

Discovering Advanced Algebra More Practice Your Skills
©2004 Key Curriculum Press

Lesson 4.1 • Interpreting Graphs

Name _____ Period _____ Date _____

1. Describe the pattern of the graph of each of the following situations as the graphs are read from left to right as *increasing, decreasing, increasing and then decreasing,* or *decreasing and then increasing.*

   a. The height of a child at birth and on each birthday from age 1 to age 6

   b. The balance that is due on a home mortgage from the date the house was purchased until it was sold 8 years later

   c. The height of a ball that is thrown upward from the top of a building from the time it is thrown until it hits the ground

   d. The monthly electric bill for August of one year to July of the next year for a family living in Atlanta, Georgia, in a home with central air conditioning. (Assume that July and August are the hottest months and that the family uses natural gas for heating.)

   e. The value of a car from the time it was purchased as a new car to the time it was traded in 5 years later

2. For each of the situations described in Exercise 1, describe the real-world meaning of the vertical intercept of the graph.

3. Sketch a graph to match each description.

   a. Decreasing steadily throughout, first slowly and then at a faster rate

   b. Increasing rapidly at a constant rate, then suddenly becoming constant, then decreasing rapidly at a constant rate

4. Sketch what you think is a reasonable graph for each relationship described. In each situation, identify the variables and label your axes appropriately.

   a. The money you earned in a week compared to the number of hours you worked in the week

   b. The temperature of a hot drink sitting on your desk

   c. Your speed as you cycle up a hill and down the other side

   d. The amount of postage charged for different weights of letters

   e. The intensity of light available for reading compared to your distance from the reading lamp

   f. The height of a hot dog wrapper after it is released by your little brother from the top row of a football stadium

Lesson 4.2 • Function Notation

Name _____ Period _____ Date _____

1. Determine whether or not each graph represents a function. Explain how you know.

   a.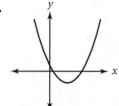
   b.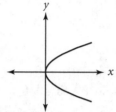
   c.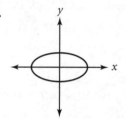

2. Find each of the indicated function values.

   a. If $f(x) = -\sqrt{4x + 1}$, find $f\left(-\frac{1}{4}\right)$, $f(0)$, $f(0.75)$, $f(2)$, and $f(12)$.

   b. If $f(x) = -x^2 + 3x + 5$, find $f(-3)$, $f(0)$, $f(2)$, $f(5)$, and $f(8)$.

   c. If $f(x) = \frac{2}{x - 4}$, find $f(-4)$, $f(0)$, $f(5)$, $f(8)$, and $f(24)$.

3. Use the graph below to find each of the following.

   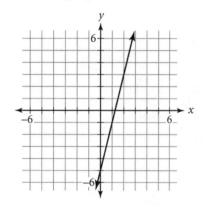

   a. $f(3) + f(-3)$
   b. $f(10) \cdot f(-2)$
   c. $f(f(10))$
   d. x when $f(x) = 19$
   e. x when $f(x) = -3$
   f. x when $f(x) = 15$
   g. x when $f(x + 2) = -9$
   h. x when $f(x - 3) = 35$
   i. x when $f(x + 4) = -21$

4. Define variables and write a function that describes each situation.

   a. You drive on an interstate highway with your cruise control set at 65 miles per hour and do not need to stop or alter your speed.

   b. You rent a small moving van to move your belongings to your new apartment. The rental company charges $45 a day plus $0.22 a mile to rent the van.

Discovering Advanced Algebra More Practice Your Skills
©2004 Key Curriculum Press

Lesson 4.3 • Lines in Motion

Name_____ Period_____ Date_____

1. Describe how each graph translates the graph of $y = f(x)$.

   a. $y = f(x) + 5$ b. $y = f(x) - 3$ c. $y = f(x - 2)$

   d. $y = f(x + 6)$ e. $y = f(x + 4) - 2$ f. $y = 5 + f(x - 7)$

2. Find each of the following.

   a. $f(x + 1)$ if $f(x) = 3x$ b. $f(x - 2)$ if $f(x) = -4x$

   c. $3 + f(x + 4)$ if $f(x) = 2x$ d. $-4 + f(x + 3)$ if $f(x) = -x$

   e. $f(x - 5)$ if $f(x) = 2x + 1$ f. $3 + f(x + 6)$ if $f(x) = 8 - x$

3. Write an equation for each line.

   a. The line $y = 2.5x$ translated up 4

   b. The line $y = -1.2x$ translated ri

   c. The line $y = -x$ translated up 5   left 2 units

   d. The line $y = \frac{1}{2}x$ translated dowr   d right 4 units

4. The graph of $y = f(x)$ is shown at   e an equation for each
   related graph showing how the fu   been translated.

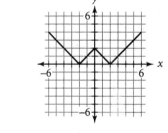

   a.
   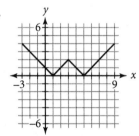

   b.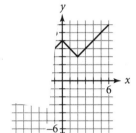

   c.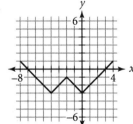

   d.

Lesson 4.4 • Translations and the Quadratic Family

Name _____ Period _____ Date _____

1. Describe the translations of the graph of $y = x^2$ needed to produce the graph of each equation.

   a. $y = x^2 - 6$ b. $y = (x + 5)^2$ c. $y = x^2 + 2.5$

   d. $y = (x - 10)^2$ e. $y = (x - 3)^2 - 9$ f. $y = (x + 7.5)^2 + 2.5$

2. Find the vertex of each parabola.

   a. $y = x^2$ b. $y = x^2 + 3$ c. $y = x^2 - 4$

   d. $y = (x - 2)^2$ e. $y = (x + 3)^2$ f. $y = (x + 1)^2 + 5$

   g. $y = (x - 4)^2 - 10$ h. $y = 4 + (x - 7)^2$ i. $y = -8 + (x + 5)^2$

3. Each parabola described is the graph of $y = x^2$. Write an equation for each parabola and sketch its graph.

   a. The parabola is translated left 3 units.

   b. The parabola is translated up 1 unit.

   c. The parabola is translated right 5 units.

   d. The parabola is translated down 4 units.

   e. The parabola is translated left 4 units and up 2 units.

   f. The parabola is translated right 2 units and down 3 units.

4. Describe what happens to the graph of $y = x^2$ in the following situations.

   a. y is replaced with $(y + 1)$. b. x is replaced with $(x - 5)$.

   c. x is replaced with $(x + 3)$. d. y is replaced with $(y - 6)$.

5. Solve.

   a. $x^2 = 49$ b. $x^2 + 6 = 31$ c. $x^2 - 12 = 52$

   d. $(x + 4)^2 = 81$ e. $(x - 3)^2 = 100$ f. $(x + 7)^2 = 144$

   g. $x^2 = 17$ h. $x^2 - 11 = 19$ i. $(x + 2)^2 = 13$

   j. $(x + 4)^2 - 5 = 31$ k. $14 + (x + 12)^2 = 35$ l. $-20 + (x - 5)^2 = 3$

Discovering Advanced Algebra More Practice Your Skills
©2004 Key Curriculum Press

Lesson 4.5 • Reflections and the Square Root Family

Name _____ Period _____ Date _____

1. Describe what happens to the graph of $y = \sqrt{x}$ in each of the following situations.

   a. x is replaced with $(x + 6)$.   b. y is replaced with $(y - 5)$.

   c. y is replaced with $(y + 1)$.   d. x is replaced with $(x - 8)$.

2. Each graph below is a transformation of the graph of either the parent function $y = x^2$ or the parent function $y = \sqrt{x}$. Write an equation for each graph.

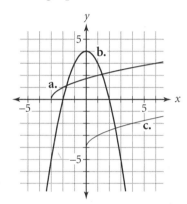
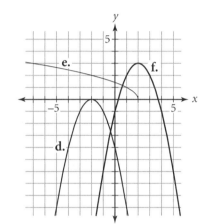

3. Given the graph of $y = f(x)$, draw a graph of each of these related functions.

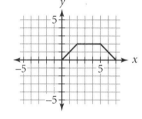

   a. $y = -f(x)$ b. $y = f(-x)$ c. $y = -f(-x)$

4. Solve each equation for y to get two separate functions that could be entered into a graphing calculator. In each case, label the equations as Y_1 and Y_2. Then combine both functions to create a single relation that involves x and y.

   a. $(y + 2)^2 = x$ b. $y^2 = x + 2$ c. $(y + 1)^2 = x - 6$

5. Use the function $h = -4.9t^2 + d$ to answer each question. (Round your answers to the nearest tenth of a second.)

   a. If a ball is dropped from a height of 500 meters, how long will it take the ball to reach a height of 200 meters?

   b. If a ball is dropped from a height of 175 meters, how long will it take the ball to reach a height of 50 meters?

   c. If a ball is dropped from a height of 90 meters, how long will it take the ball to hit the ground?

Lesson 4.6 • Stretches and Shrinks and the Absolute-Value Family

Name _____ **Period** _____ **Date** _____

1. Each graph is a transformation of one of the parent functions you've studied. Write an equation for each graph.

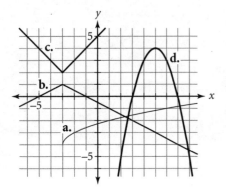

2. Describe the transformations of the graph of $y = |x|$ needed to produce the graph of each equation.

   a. $y = |x - 3|$ **b.** $y = -|x|$ **c.** $y = |-x|$

   d. $y = \left|\dfrac{x}{4}\right|$ **e.** $y = 3|x|$ **f.** $y = |3x|$

   g. $y = -|x| + 5$ **h.** $y = |x + 2| - 1$ **i.** $y = 1.5\left|\dfrac{x}{2}\right|$

   j. $\dfrac{y}{0.5} = -|x|$ **k.** $y = -3|x + 4| + 6$ **l.** $\dfrac{y}{2} = |x - 1| - 2$

3. Find the vertex of the graph of each equation in Exercise 2 and sketch the graph.

4. Solve.

   a. $|x| = 9$ **b.** $|x + 2| = 5$ **c.** $|x - 5| - 7 = 0$

   d. $|x + 2| + 5 = 4$ **e.** $3|x - 5| - 2 = 10$ **f.** $\left|\dfrac{x}{2}\right| + 5 = 12$

5. Solve each equation for y.

   a. $\dfrac{y}{2} = \left|\dfrac{x}{4}\right|$ **b.** $y - 2 = -4(x + 1)^2$ **c.** $\dfrac{y}{-3} = \sqrt{x} + 1.5$

   d. $\dfrac{y - 3}{2} = (x + 1)^2$ **e.** $\dfrac{y + 1}{-3} = \sqrt{x + 2}$ **f.** $\dfrac{y - 5}{3} = \left|\dfrac{x + 2}{4}\right|$

Discovering Advanced Algebra More Practice Your Skills
©2004 Key Curriculum Press

Lesson 4.7 • Transformations and the Circle Family

Name _____ Period _____ Date _____

1. Solve each equation for y to get two separate equations that could be entered into a graphing calculator. In each case, label the two equations as Y1 and Y2.

   a. $x^2 + y^2 = 4$ b. $4x^2 + y^2 = 9$ c. $3x - 2y^2 = 1$

2. Write an equation for each circle.

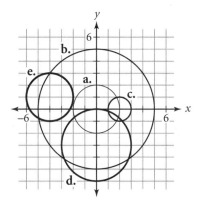

3. If $f(x) = \sqrt{1 - x^2}$, write an equation for each of the following related functions.

   a. $-f(x)$ b. $f(-x)$ c. $2f(x)$ d. $f(2x)$

4. Without graphing, find the x- and y-intercepts of the graph of each equation.

   a. $x^2 + y^2 = 1$ b. $y = \sqrt{1 - x^2}$ c. $y = -\sqrt{1 - x^2}$

   d. $y = 3\sqrt{1 - x^2}$ e. $y = -2\sqrt{1 - x^2}$ f. $y = \sqrt{1 - (2x)^2}$

   g. $y = -2\sqrt{1 - (4x)^2}$ h. $y = -\sqrt{1 - \left(\dfrac{x}{3}\right)^2}$ i. $y = 2\sqrt{1 - \left(\dfrac{x}{4}\right)^2}$

5. Write an equation for each transformation of the unit circle, and identify its graph as a circle or an ellipse. Then sketch the graph.

   a. Replace x with $(x - 2)$.   b. Replace y with $(y + 4)$.

   c. Replace y with $\dfrac{y}{3}$.   d. Replace x with $\dfrac{x}{4}$.

   e. Replace x with $\dfrac{x}{2}$ and y with $\dfrac{y}{2}$.   f. Replace x with $\dfrac{x}{4}$ and y with $\dfrac{y}{3}$.

Lesson 4.8 • Compositions of Functions

Name _____ Period _____ Date _____

1. The functions f and g are defined by sets of input and output values.

   $f = \{(5, 0), (-1, 1), (-3, 4), (1, 2), (3, 4), (-2, 6)\}$

   $g = \{(4, -1), (0, -2), (1, -1), (2, -2), (6, 0)\}$

   a. Find $f(-3)$, $f(1)$, and $f(5)$.　　b. Find $g(0)$, $g(2)$, and $g(4)$.　　c. What is the domain of f?

   d. What is the range of g?　　e. Find $f(g(4))$.　　f. Find $g(f(-3))$.

   g. Find $f(g(f(5)))$.　　h. Find $g(f(g(0)))$.

2. Use these three functions to find each value: $f(x) = -3x + 5$, $g(x) = (x - 2)^2$, $h(x) = x^2 + 4$.

   a. $f(x + 2)$　　b. $g(2x) + 1$　　c. $h(x - 1) + 3$　　d. $f(g(6))$

   e. $h(f(7))$　　f. $g(h(-5))$　　g. $f(g(h(-2)))$　　h. $g(h(f(4)))$

   i. $h(g(f(0)))$　　j. $f(h(a))$　　k. $h(f(a))$　　l. $g(h(a))$

3. For each graph below:

   i. Write an equation for the graph.

   ii. Write two functions, f and g, such that the figure is the graph of $f(g(x))$.

   a. 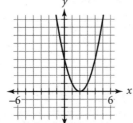　　b. 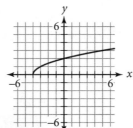　　c.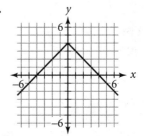

4. Marla, Shamim, and Julie went out for dinner together. The sales tax on the meal was 6%, and they agreed to leave a 15% tip. Marla thought they should calculate the tip by finding 15% of the total bill, including the sales tax. Shamim thought they should calculate the tip by finding 15% of the bill before the tax was added. Julie thought it wouldn't make any difference. Let x represent the cost of the meal in dollars before tax and tip are added.

   a. Find a function f that gives the cost of the meal, including sales tax but not the tip.

   b. Find a function g that gives the amount of the tip calculated the way Shamim suggested.

   c. Use composition to find a function that gives the amount of the tip calculated the way Marla suggested.

   d. If the cost of the meal before tax was $50, find the amount they will leave as a tip, calculated Marla's way and Shamim's way.

Lesson 5.1 • Exponential Functions

Name _____ Period _____ Date _____

1. Evaluate each function at the given value. Round to four decimal places if necessary.

   a. $f(x) = 250(0.5)^x$, $x = 3$

   b. $g(x) = 45.5(0.85)^x$, $x = 5$

   c. $h(t) = 8.72(1.02)^t$, $t = 10$

   d. $h(y) = 35(1.3)^y$, $y = 7$

   e. $r(t) = 325(1 + 0.035)^t$, $t = 8$

   f. $j(x) = 59.5(1 - 0.095)^x$, $x = 10$

   g. $k(z) = 895(1.0675)^z$, $z = 20$

   h. $q(z) = 2500(1.001)^z$, $z = 6$

2. Record the next three terms for each sequence. Then write an explicit function for the sequence.

   a. $u_0 = 12$
      $u_n = 0.8u_{n-1}$ where $n \geq 1$

   b. $u_0 = 45$
      $u_n = 1.2u_{n-1}$ where $n \geq 1$

   c. $u_0 = 50.5$
      $u_n = 2.1u_{n-1}$ where $n \geq 1$

   d. $u_0 = 256$
      $u_n = 0.65u_{n-1}$ where $n \geq 1$

3. Evaluate each function at $x = 0$, $x = 1$, and $x = 2$. Then write a recursive formula for the pattern.

   a. $f(x) = 5(3)^x$

   b. $f(x) = 250(0.5)^x$

   c. $f(x) = 15.5(1.1)^x$

   d. $f(x) = 0.75(2.2)^x$

   e. $f(x) = 575(0.08)^x$

   f. $f(x) = 66(1.01)^x$

4. Indicate whether each equation is a model for exponential growth or decay.

   a. $f(x) = 2000(0.9)^x$

   b. $f(x) = 0.8(1.2)^x$

   c. $f(x) = 3000000(2.5)^x$

   d. $f(x) = 8.2(1 - 0.22)^x$

   e. $f(x) = 3000(1 + 0.001)^x$

   f. $f(x) = 0.1(1 - 0.5)^x$

5. Calculate the ratio of the second term to the first term, and express the answer as a decimal value. State the percent increase or decrease.

   a. 80, 60

   b. 40, 45

   c. 88, 198

   d. 36, 32

   e. 110, 96.8

   f. 63, 100.8

6. Rohit bought a new car for $17,500. The value of the car is depreciating at a rate of 16% a year.

   a. Write a recursive formula that models this situation. Let u_0 represent the purchase price, u_1 represent the value of the car after 1 year, and so on.

   b. Make a table recording the value of the car after 1 year, 2 years, 3 years, 4 years, and 5 years. (Round values to the nearest dollar.)

   c. Define variables and write an exponential equation that models this situation.

Lesson 5.2 • Properties of Exponents and Power Functions

Name _____ Period _____ Date _____

1. Rewrite each expression as a fraction without exponents. Verify that your answer is equivalent to the original expression using your calculator.

   a. 3^{-2}

   b. 4^{-3}

   c. 5^{-4}

   d. 25^{-1}

   e. 7^{-3}

   f. 10^{-6}

   g. -4^{-4}

   h. $(-4)^{-4}$

   i. $(-5)^{-3}$

   j. $\left(\dfrac{1}{2}\right)^{-5}$

   k. $-\left(\dfrac{3}{5}\right)^{-2}$

   l. $\left(-\dfrac{5}{6}\right)^{-2}$

2. Rewrite each expression in the form x^n or ax^n.

   a. $x^5 \cdot x^8$

   b. $x^{12} \cdot x^{-5}$

   c. $x^{-10} \cdot x^{-5}$

   d. $4x^0 \cdot 9x^8$

   e. $\left(-10x^{-8}\right)\left(-12x^{-3}\right)$

   f. $\left(8x^{-6}\right)\left(-15x^{-14}\right)$

   g. $\dfrac{x^9}{x^{-9}}$

   h. $\dfrac{-88x^{10}}{-8x^3}$

   i. $\dfrac{35x^0}{25x^{-5}}$

   j. $\left(\dfrac{x^{-8}}{x^{-9}}\right)^2$

   k. $\left(\dfrac{-35x^7}{-7x^2}\right)^3$

   l. $\left(\dfrac{40x^{-8}}{-8x^{-2}}\right)^{-3}$

3. Solve.

   a. $2^x = \dfrac{1}{32}$

   b. $125^x = 25$

   c. $3^x = \dfrac{1}{81}$

   d. $\left(\dfrac{1}{2}\right)^x = 128$

   e. $\left(\dfrac{4}{9}\right)^x = \dfrac{81}{16}$

   f. $\left(\dfrac{1}{8}\right)^x = \dfrac{1}{16}$

4. Solve each equation. If answers are not exact, approximate them to two decimal places.

   a. $x^5 = 895$

   b. $x^{0.8} = 45$

   c. $x^{-3} = 1234$

   d. $6x^{1.5} = 80$

   e. $20x^{1/2} - 8 = 4.5$

   f. $5x^{-1/3} = 0.06$

   g. $8x^9 = 6x^6$

   h. $15x^{-3} = 10x^{-2}$

   i. $200x^{-1} = 125x^{-3}$

Lesson 5.3 • Rational Exponents and Roots

Name _____ Period _____ Date _____

1. Identify each function as a power function, an exponential function, or neither of these. (It may be translated, stretched, or reflected.)

   a. $f(x) = 2^x$ **b.** $f(x) = x^2 - 2x + 3$ **c.** $f(x) = 0.5x^3 - 4$

   d. $f(x) = \dfrac{1}{3^x}$ **e.** $f(x) = \dfrac{1}{x} + 2$ **f.** $f(x) = \dfrac{1}{2x^2 - x}$

2. Rewrite each expression in the form b^x in which x is a rational exponent.

   a. $\sqrt[4]{b}$ **b.** $\sqrt{c^3}$ **c.** $\sqrt[5]{d^7}$

   d. $\dfrac{1}{\sqrt[3]{a}}$ **e.** $\left(\sqrt[3]{d}\right)^4$ **f.** $\dfrac{1}{\sqrt{r^5}}$

3. Solve each equation. If answers are not exact, approximate them to the nearest hundredth.

   a. $\sqrt[5]{x} = 12$ **b.** $\sqrt[3]{x^2} = 5.5$ **c.** $\sqrt[5]{x^3} = 27$

   d. $\dfrac{1}{\sqrt{x}} = 0.77$ **e.** $\sqrt{8x^3} = 20$ **f.** $4\sqrt[3]{x} + 18 = 32$

   g. $\sqrt[5]{x^3} - 23 = -15$ **h.** $\sqrt[3]{4x^2} + 8.5 = 19.8$ **i.** $\sqrt[8]{x^5} = 12.75$

4. Each of the following graphs is a transformation of the power function $y = x^{3/2}$. Write the equation for each curve.

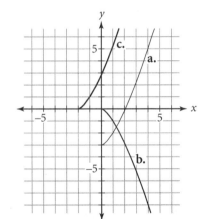
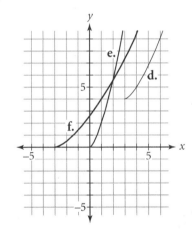

Lesson 5.4 • Applications of Exponential and Power Equations

Name _____ Period _____ Date _____

1. Solve each equation. If answers are not exact, approximate them to the nearest hundredth.

   a. $x^4 = 48$

   b. $\sqrt[3]{x} = 2.6$

   c. $x^{2/3} = 8.75$

   d. $x^{-1/4} = 0.2$

   e. $0.75x^5 - 8 = -3$

   f. $4\left(x^{5/6} + 7\right) = 159$

   g. $128.5 = 36 \cdot x^{2.5}$

   h. $224 = 200\left(1 + \dfrac{x}{4}\right)^9$

   i. $1500\left(1 + \dfrac{x}{12}\right)^{6.5} = 1525$

2. Rewrite each expression in the form ax^n.

   a. $\left(8x^9\right)^{2/3}$

   b. $\left(81x^{12}\right)^{3/4}$

   c. $\left(49x^{-10}\right)^{1/2}$

   d. $\left(-27x^{-9}\right)^{4/3}$

   e. $\left(100{,}000x^{10}\right)^{3/5}$

   f. $\left(-125x^{-15}\right)^{1/3}$

   g. $\left(-216x^9\right)^{4/3}$

   h. $\left(16x^{28}\right)^{-5/4}$

   i. $\left(-32x^{-30}\right)^{-6/5}$

3. Give the average annual rate of inflation for each situation described. Give your answers to the nearest tenth of a percent.

   a. The cost of a 20-ounce box of cereal increased from $4.25 to $5.50 over 5 years.

   b. The cost of a gallon of milk increased from $2.75 to $3.40 over 3 years.

   c. The cost of a movie ticket increased from $6.00 to $8.50 over 10 years.

   d. The monthly rent for Hector's apartment increased from $650 to $757 over 4 years.

   e. The starting hourly wage for a salesclerk increased from $5.85 to $7.65 over 6 years.

   f. The value of an antique table increased from $3500 to $5700 over 7 years.

4. The population of a small town has been declining because jobs have been leaving the area. The population was 23,000 in 1996 and 18,750 in 2001. Assume that the population is decreasing exponentially.

   a. Define variables and write an equation that models the population in this town in a particular year.

   b. Use your model to predict the population in 2004.

   c. According to your model, in what year will the population first fall below 12,000?

Discovering Advanced Algebra More Practice Your Skills
©2004 Key Curriculum Press

Lesson 5.5 • Building Inverses of Functions

Name _____ Period _____ Date _____

1. Each of the functions below has an inverse that is also a function. Find four points on the graph of each function f, using the given values of x. Use these points to find four points on the graph of f^{-1}.

   a. $f(x) = 3x - 4$; $x = -2, 0, \frac{4}{3}, 4$

   b. $f(x) = x^3 - 2$; $x = -3, -1, 2, 5$

2. Given $h(t) = 15 - 3t$, find each value.

   a. $h(4)$

   b. $h(1.5)$

   c. $h^{-1}(0)$

   d. $h^{-1}(1.5)$

3. For each function below, determine whether or not the inverse of this function is a function. Find the equation of the inverse and graph both equations on the same axes.

   a. $y = -2x + 5$

   b. $y = |x|$

   c. $y = x^2 - 4$

   d. $y = -\sqrt{1 - x^2}$

   e. $y = x^3$

   f. $y = -(x + 3)^2$

4. Balloons and Laughs Inc. is a small company that entertains at children's birthday parties. B & L uses a complicated formula to calculate its prices, taking into account all of its costs. The price equation is $p(x) = 4\sqrt[3]{(8x + 3)^2} + 25$, where x is the number of person-hours supplied for the party at a price of $p(x)$. For example, if $x = 4$, four clowns will come for one hour, two clowns will come for two hours, or one clown will come for four hours.

   a. What is the price if two clowns come to a party for 90 minutes?

   b. Many customers want to know what they can get for a particular amount of money. Rewrite the price equation for B & L so that it can input the amount of money a customer wants to spend and the output will be the number of person-hours they will get for their money. Call the new function $p^{-1}(x)$.

   c. B & L's Ultimate Party costs $125. How many person-hours do you get at an Ultimate Party?

Lesson 5.6 • Logarithmic Functions

Name _____ Period _____ Date _____

1. Write an equation for the inverse of each function.

   a. $f(x) = 5^x$ **b.** $f(x) = \log_2 x$ **c.** $f(x) = \log x$

2. Rewrite each logarithmic equation in exponential form using the definition of logarithm. Then solve for x.

   a. $\log_2 128 = x$ **b.** $\log_3 \dfrac{1}{81} = x$ **c.** $x = \log 0.001$

   d. $\log_{12} \sqrt[4]{12} = x$ **e.** $x = \log_4 32$ **f.** $\log 1 = x$

   g. $x = \log_5 125$ **h.** $\log_8 1 = x$ **i.** $\log_{20} 20 = x$

   j. $\log_4 \dfrac{1}{16} = x$ **k.** $x = \log_9 \sqrt[3]{9}$ **l.** $x = \log 0.00001$

3. Find the exact value of each logarithm without using a calculator. Write answers as integers or fractions in lowest terms.

   a. $\log_2 8$ **b.** $\log_3 81$ **c.** $\log_7 49$

   d. $\log_5 \sqrt{5}$ **e.** $\log_3 \dfrac{1}{3}$ **f.** $\log_2 \dfrac{1}{32}$

   g. $\log_4 8$ **h.** $\log_8 4$ **i.** $\log 1{,}000{,}000{,}000$

4. Each graph is a transformation of either $y = 10^x$ or $y = \log x$. Write the equation for each graph.

   a.
   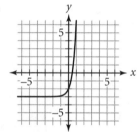
   b.
   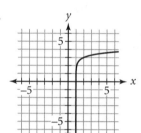
   c.
   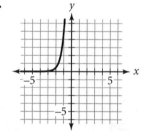

5. Use the change-of-base property to solve each equation. (Round to four decimal places.)

   a. $\log_4 9 = x$ **b.** $\log_5 120 = x$ **c.** $\log_3 0.9 = x$

   d. $3^x = 21$ **e.** $4^x = 99$ **f.** $6^x = 729$

   g. $2^x = 1.5$ **h.** $7^x = 4.88$ **i.** $12^x = 5.75$

   j. $5^x = 0.75$ **k.** $8^x = 0.523$ **l.** $20^x = 0.04$

Discovering Advanced Algebra More Practice Your Skills
©2004 Key Curriculum Press

Lesson 5.7 • Properties of Logarithms

Name _____ Period _____ Date _____

1. Change the form of each expression below using properties of logarithms or exponents. Name each property you use.

   a. $\log r - \log s$

   b. $\left(x^y\right)^z$

   c. $\dfrac{1}{a^b}$

   d. $\log_r s$

   e. q^{a+b}

   f. $\log_b x^m$

   g. $(cd)^m$

   h. $\log_b xy$

   i. $\left(\dfrac{r}{s}\right)^m$

   j. $c^{m/n}$

   k. $\dfrac{\log_a x}{\log_a y}$

   l. $t\log_a y$

2. Determine whether each equation is true or false.

   a. $\log 45 = \log 5 + \log 9$

   b. $\log 8 = \dfrac{\log 32}{\log 4}$

   c. $\log_5 9 - \log_5 2 = \log_5 4.5$

   d. $\log 32 = \dfrac{1}{5}\log 2$

   e. $\log 12 - \log 4 = \log 8$

   f. $\log\dfrac{1}{5} = \dfrac{1}{\log 5}$

   g. $\log 4 = \dfrac{2}{3}\log 8$

   h. $\log \sqrt[3]{5} = \dfrac{1}{3}\log 5$

   i. $\log_2 \dfrac{1}{81} = -2\log_2 9$

   j. $\log \sqrt{6} = -2\log 6$

   k. $\log 75 = 3\log 25$

   l. $\log_3 15 - \log_3 5 = 1$

3. Write each expression as a sum or difference of logarithms (or constants times logarithms). Simplify the result if possible.

   a. $\log xyz$

   b. $\log_2 \dfrac{xy}{z}$

   c. $\log \dfrac{p^2}{q^3}$

   d. $\log_5 \dfrac{a\sqrt{b}}{c^4}$

   e. $\log_4\left(\sqrt{r} \cdot \sqrt[3]{s} \cdot \sqrt[4]{t^3}\right)$

   f. $\log_3\left(\dfrac{\sqrt[3]{abc}}{\sqrt[4]{x}}\right)$

4. Solve each equation. (Round answers to the nearest hundredth.)

   a. $5.2^x = 375$

   b. $82 + 2.5^x = 130$

   c. $32(0.87)^x = 260$

   d. $48(1.04)^x = 90$

   e. $32 + 16(1.035)^x = 315$

   f. $105 + 30(0.95)^x = 210$

Lesson 5.8 • Applications of Logarithms

Name _____ Period _____ Date _____

1. Solve each equation. Round answers that are not exact to four decimal places.

   a. $10^x = 650$ **b.** $19683 = 3^x$ **c.** $0.5^x = 64$

   d. $9.5(8^x) = 220$ **e.** $0.405 = 15.6(0.72)^x$ **f.** $32(1.08)^x = 275$

2. Suppose that you invest \$5000 in a savings account. How long would it take you to double your money under each of the following conditions?

   a. 5% interest compounded annually

   b. 6% interest compounded quarterly

   c. 5.4% interest compounded twice annually

   d. 3.6% interest compounded monthly

   e. 6.75% interest compounded quarterly

   f. 4.5% interest compounded monthly

3. The Richter scale rating of the magnitude of an earthquake is given by the formula $\log\left(\frac{I}{I_0}\right)$, where I_0 is a certain small magnitude used as a reference point. (Richter scale ratings are given to the nearest tenth.)

   a. Find the Richter scale rating for an earthquake with magnitude $100,000 I_0$.

   b. Find the Richter scale rating for an earthquake with magnitude $2,000,000 I_0$.

   c. A devastating earthquake occurred in western Turkey in 1999, resulting in about 17,000 deaths. This earthquake measured 7.4 on the Richter scale. Express the magnitude of this earthquake as a multiple of I_0.

   d. Another earthquake in 1998, centered in Adana, Turkey, caused 144 deaths. This earthquake measured 6.3 on the Richter scale. Express the magnitude of this earthquake as a multiple of I_0.

   e. Compare the magnitudes of the two earthquakes in Turkey described in 3c and d.

4. The population of an animal species introduced into an area sometimes increases rapidly at first and then more slowly over time. A logarithmic function models this kind of growth. Suppose that a population of N deer in an area t months after the deer are introduced is given by the equation $N = 325 \log(4t + 2)$.

   a. Use this model to predict the deer population 3 months, 6 months, 12 months, and 18 months after the deer are introduced.

   b. According to this model, how long will it take for the deer population to reach 800? Round to the nearest whole month.

Discovering Advanced Algebra More Practice Your Skills
©2004 Key Curriculum Press

Lesson 6.1 • Matrix Representations

Name _____ Period _____ Date _____

1. Supply the missing entries in each transition matrix.

   a. $[M] = \begin{bmatrix} .7 & m_{12} \\ m_{21} & .2 \end{bmatrix}$

   b. $[R] = \begin{bmatrix} r_{11} & .09 \\ .73 & r_{22} \end{bmatrix}$

   c. $[T] = \begin{bmatrix} t_{11} & .22 \\ t_{21} & .68 \end{bmatrix}$

2. A survey of registered voters showed that of those people who voted in the 2000 presidential election, 87% expect to vote in the 2004 election, while of those who did not vote in the 2000 presidential election, 22% expect to vote in the 2004 election.

   a. Complete the following transition diagram to represent the survey results.

   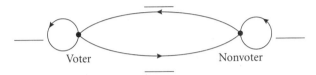

   b. Write a transition matrix that conveys the same information as your transition diagram. List voters first and nonvoters second.

   c. Suppose that the survey includes 300 people who voted in 2000 and 300 who did not. Based on this information, how many of these people would you expect to vote in 2004?

3. Matrix $[M]$ represents the vertices of $\triangle DEF$.

   $$[M] = \begin{bmatrix} -5 & 2 & 4 \\ 3 & 0 & -6 \end{bmatrix}$$

   a. Name the coordinates of the vertices and draw the triangle.

   b. What matrix represents the image of $\triangle DEF$ after a translation left 3 units?

   c. What matrix represents the image of $\triangle DEF$ after a translation right 4 units and down 2 units?

   d. What matrix represents the image of $\triangle DEF$ after a reflection across the y-axis?

   e. What matrix represents the image of $\triangle DEF$ after a reflection across the x-axis?

   f. What matrix represents the image of $\triangle DEF$ after a reflection across the line $y = x$?

Lesson 6.2 • Matrix Operations

Name _____ Period _____ Date _____

1. Find the missing values.

   a. $[3 \quad 12 \quad -8] + [9 \quad -12 \quad 13] = [x \quad y \quad z]$

   b. $\begin{bmatrix} 24 & -15 \\ 9 & 19 \end{bmatrix} - \begin{bmatrix} 26 & -10 \\ -8 & 32 \end{bmatrix} = \begin{bmatrix} a & b \\ c & d \end{bmatrix}$

   c. $-5\begin{bmatrix} 3.8 & -5.2 \\ -1.9 & 0.8 \end{bmatrix} = \begin{bmatrix} n_{11} & n_{12} \\ n_{21} & n_{22} \end{bmatrix}$

   d. $3\begin{bmatrix} 5 & -4 \\ -8 & 2 \end{bmatrix} + 7\begin{bmatrix} -5 & 0 \\ 5 & -6 \end{bmatrix} = \begin{bmatrix} a & b \\ c & d \end{bmatrix}$

2. Perform the following matrix arithmetic problems. If a problem is impossible, explain why.

   a. $\begin{bmatrix} 8.5 & 4.2 \\ 3.6 & -2.7 \end{bmatrix} - \begin{bmatrix} 7.9 & 8.8 \\ 2.9 & -0.9 \end{bmatrix}$
   b. $\begin{bmatrix} 1 & 0 & 2 \\ -1 & 4 & 5 \\ 0 & 1 & 3 \end{bmatrix}\begin{bmatrix} 10 \\ -8 \\ 4 \end{bmatrix}$

   c. $\begin{bmatrix} 12 & -14 & 10 \\ -6 & 18 & 5 \end{bmatrix} + \begin{bmatrix} -12 & -6 \\ 14 & 18 \\ -10 & 5 \end{bmatrix}$
   d. $[2 \quad -5]\begin{bmatrix} 3 & -6 \\ 5 & 0 \\ -1 & 4 \end{bmatrix}$

   e. $\begin{bmatrix} 0.5 & -0.2 \\ 0.4 & 0.1 \end{bmatrix}\begin{bmatrix} 30 \\ 40 \end{bmatrix}$
   f. $0.5\begin{bmatrix} 20 & -10 \\ 16 & 14 \end{bmatrix} + 2.5\begin{bmatrix} 12 & -8 \\ -16 & 30 \end{bmatrix}$

3. This matrix represents a triangle.

$$\begin{bmatrix} -2 & 2 & -1 \\ -3 & 0 & 3 \end{bmatrix}$$

   a. Graph the triangle. Label the vertices with their coordinates.

   b. Find the answer to this matrix multiplication:

$$\begin{bmatrix} 0 & 1 \\ 1 & 0 \end{bmatrix}\begin{bmatrix} -2 & 2 & -1 \\ -3 & 0 & 3 \end{bmatrix}$$

   c. Graph the image represented by the matrix in 3b.

   d. Describe the transformation.

Discovering Advanced Algebra More Practice Your Skills
©2004 Key Curriculum Press

Lesson 6.3 • Row Reduction Method

Name _____ Period _____ Date _____

1. Write a system of equations for each augmented matrix.

a. $\begin{bmatrix} 3 & -1 & | & 5 \\ 1 & 4 & | & -2 \end{bmatrix}$ b. $\begin{bmatrix} 4 & -1 & 1 & | & 6 \\ -2 & 3 & -2 & | & 5 \\ 3 & 4 & -4 & | & 0 \end{bmatrix}$ c. $\begin{bmatrix} 3 & -4 & 0 & | & 2 \\ -1 & 0 & 3 & | & 0 \\ -2 & 5 & 0 & | & -1 \end{bmatrix}$

2. Write an augmented matrix for each system.

a. $\begin{cases} x + 2y = 8 \\ 2x - y = 1 \end{cases}$ b. $\begin{cases} x + y - z = 0 \\ 2x + 3y - 3z = -3 \\ -x - 2y + 2z = 3 \end{cases}$ c. $\begin{cases} 2x + z = 8 \\ 3y - 4z = -1 \\ 4x - y = 3 \end{cases}$

3. Perform the given row operation on each matrix.

a. $\begin{bmatrix} 4 & -2 & | & 5 \\ 0 & -3 & | & 12 \end{bmatrix}; \dfrac{R_2}{-3} \to R_2$

b. $\begin{bmatrix} 1 & 3 & 5 & | & -2 \\ 3 & -4 & 2 & | & 0 \\ -2 & 4 & 6 & | & 1 \end{bmatrix}; -3R_1 + R_2 \to R_2$

c. $\begin{bmatrix} 1 & -3 & 4 & | & -2 \\ 3 & 1 & -2 & | & 0 \\ -2 & 5 & -6 & | & 1 \end{bmatrix}; 2R_1 + R_3 \to R_3$

d. $\begin{bmatrix} -\dfrac{2}{3} & \dfrac{1}{6} & -\dfrac{5}{6} & | & -2 \\ 4 & -2 & 0 & | & 4 \\ -\dfrac{3}{4} & -\dfrac{5}{8} & \dfrac{7}{16} & | & -5 \end{bmatrix}; 16R_3 \to R_3$

4. Three kinds of tickets were sold for a concert. Main floor tickets cost $35, balcony tickets cost $25, and gallery tickets cost $15. The box office sold 475 tickets for a total of $13,275. There were 45 more main floor tickets sold than balcony tickets.

a. Let m represent the number of main floor tickets sold, b represent the number of balcony tickets sold, and g represent the number of gallery tickets sold. Write a system of equations that you can use to find how many tickets of each kind were sold.

b. Rewrite your system of equations as an augmented matrix.

c. Apply row operations to your matrix to transform it into reduced row-echelon form.

d. How many tickets of each kind were sold?

Lesson 6.4 • Solving Systems with Inverse Matrices

Name _____ Period _____ Date _____

1. Rewrite each matrix equation as a system of equations.

a. $\begin{bmatrix} 4 & -3 \\ 2 & 6 \end{bmatrix}\begin{bmatrix} x \\ y \end{bmatrix} = \begin{bmatrix} 5 \\ -1 \end{bmatrix}$

b. $\begin{bmatrix} 0.5 & 0.8 \\ 0.1 & -0.2 \end{bmatrix}\begin{bmatrix} x \\ y \end{bmatrix} = \begin{bmatrix} 4 \\ 1.5 \end{bmatrix}$

c. $\begin{bmatrix} 2 & -4 & 0 \\ 5 & 0 & 3 \\ 0 & 6 & -1 \end{bmatrix}\begin{bmatrix} x \\ y \\ z \end{bmatrix} = \begin{bmatrix} 1 \\ 2 \\ 3 \end{bmatrix}$

2. Rewrite each system in matrix form.

a. $\begin{cases} 4x - 3y = 8 \\ 3x + 2y = -8 \end{cases}$

b. $\begin{cases} x + 7y + z = -1 \\ -5x - 14y - z = -4 \\ 5x + y - 2z = 0 \end{cases}$

c. $\begin{cases} 2x + 3y - z = -5 \\ 3x + 4z = -1 \\ y - 2z = -3 \end{cases}$

3. Determine whether or not the matrices in each pair are inverses.

a. $\begin{bmatrix} 2 & -3 \\ 5 & -8 \end{bmatrix}, \begin{bmatrix} -8 & 3 \\ -5 & 2 \end{bmatrix}$

b. $\begin{bmatrix} 4 & 5 \\ 2 & 3 \end{bmatrix}, \begin{bmatrix} 1.5 & -2.5 \\ -1 & 2 \end{bmatrix}$

c. $\begin{bmatrix} \frac{1}{2} & -\frac{1}{4} \\ 4 & 2 \end{bmatrix}, \begin{bmatrix} 1 & \frac{1}{8} \\ -2 & \frac{1}{4} \end{bmatrix}$

d. $\begin{bmatrix} 1 & 0 & -1 \\ 0 & 1 & 1 \\ 1 & 1 & 1 \end{bmatrix}, \begin{bmatrix} 0 & -1 & 1 \\ 1 & 2 & -1 \\ -1 & -1 & 1 \end{bmatrix}$

e. $\begin{bmatrix} 1 & 1 & 0 \\ 1 & 0 & 1 \\ 0 & 0 & 1 \end{bmatrix}, \begin{bmatrix} 0 & 1 & 1 \\ 1 & 1 & 1 \\ 0 & 0 & 1 \end{bmatrix}$

4. Find the inverse of each matrix if the inverse exists.

a. $\begin{bmatrix} 3 & -5 \\ -2 & 4 \end{bmatrix}$

b. $\begin{bmatrix} 4 & -6 \\ 2 & -3 \end{bmatrix}$

c. $\begin{bmatrix} 1 & 0 & -1 \\ 2 & 1 & 0 \\ 0 & -2 & 1 \end{bmatrix}$

5. Rolando bought 4 CDs and 5 DVDs for a total of $146. Suzanna bought 6 CDs and 3 DVDs for a total of $138. All the CDs were one price and all the DVDs were one price.

a. Let c represent the price of a CD and d represent the price of a DVD. Write a system of equations that you can use to find the prices.

b. Rewrite your system in matrix form, $[A][X] = [B]$.

c. Write an equivalent matrix equation in the form $[X] = [A]^{-1}[B]$.

d. Use matrix multiplication to find $[X]$.

e. What was the cost of 1 CD and the cost of 1 DVD?

Discovering Advanced Algebra More Practice Your Skills
©2004 Key Curriculum Press

Lesson 6.5 • Systems of Linear Inequalities

Name _____ Period _____ Date _____

1. Solve each inequality for y.

   a. $3x + 4y < 12$ b. $4x - 5y \leq 20$ c. $3 + 2(x - 4y) > 12$

2. Graph each linear inequality.

   a. $y < -x + 5$ b. $y > \frac{1}{3}x - 3$ c. $y \leq 3x - 4$

   d. $2x + 3y < 6$ e. $3x - 5y \geq 0$ f. $4y - 2x \leq -8$

3. Graph the feasible region of each system of inequalities. Find the coordinates of each vertex.

   a. $\begin{cases} y \leq x \\ y \leq -x + 7 \\ x \geq 0 \\ y \geq 0 \end{cases}$
   b. $\begin{cases} x + y \leq 8 \\ x + y \geq 5 \\ x \geq 0 \\ y \geq 0 \end{cases}$
   c. $\begin{cases} x - 3y \geq -11 \\ x - 3y \leq -2 \\ 1 \leq x \leq 4 \end{cases}$

   d. $\begin{cases} y \geq x^2 \\ y \leq x + 2 \\ x \geq 0 \\ y \geq 0 \end{cases}$
   e. $\begin{cases} y \leq -|x| + 4 \\ y \leq 3x \\ x \geq 0 \\ y \geq 0 \end{cases}$
   f. $\begin{cases} y \leq \sqrt{25 - x^2} \\ y \geq 0.75x \\ x \geq 0 \end{cases}$

4. Write an inequality to represent each constraint.

   a. Marta's schedule allows her to spend no more than 15 hours a week studying algebra and history. Each algebra assignment takes 1.5 hours, and each history assignment takes 1.25 hours. Let a represent the number of algebra assignments she completes and h represent the number of history assignments she completes in a week.

   b. A company is shipping kitchen appliances to a store. Each shipment contains full-size food processors, which weigh 10 pounds each, and mini food processors, which weigh 2.5 pounds each. The maximum weight permitted for one shipment is 460 pounds. Let m represent the number of mini food processors and f represent the number of full-size food processors.

   c. Leo is taking an algebra test containing computation problems worth 5 points each and application problems worth 8 points each. Leo needs to score at least 83 points on the test to maintain his B average. Let c represent the number of computation problems he answers correctly and a represent the number of application problems he answers correctly.

Lesson 6.6 • Linear Programming

Name _____ Period _____ Date _____

1. For each situation, write the expression that should be optimized and tell whether the expression should be minimized or maximized.

   a. A yoga teacher sells yoga mats for $25 each and yoga videos for $14 each. If x represents the number of mats she sells and y represents the number of videos she sells, represent the amount of money she receives from selling mats and videos.

   b. A company manufactures calculators. The company's profits are $15 per graphing calculator and $6 per scientific calculator. If x represents the number of graphing calculators sold and y represents the number of scientific calculators sold, represent the company's profits from selling the two types of calculators.

   c. A school purchases classroom supplies, spending $3.25 per ream (500 sheets) of paper and $2.75 per box of pencils. If x represents the number of boxes of pencils purchased and y represents the number of reams of paper purchased, represent the school's costs for the supplies.

2. You would like to maximize profits at your bakery, which makes decorated sheet cakes for parties in two sizes, a full sheet and a half sheet. A batch of 12 full-sheet cakes takes 3.5 hours of oven time and 3 hours of decorating time, while a batch of 20 half-sheet cakes takes 5 hours of oven time and 4 hours of decorating time. The oven is available for a maximum of 21 hours a day, and the decorating room is available for 14 hours a day. Let x represent the number of batches of sheet cakes that the bakery produces in one day, and let y represent the number of batches of half-sheet cakes. The bakery makes a profit of $30 on each batch of full-sheet cakes and $35 on each batch of half-sheet cakes.

   a. Write a constraint about oven time.

   b. Write a constraint about decorating time.

   c. Write a system of inequalities that includes the constraints you have found and any commonsense constraints.

   d. Graph the feasible region and find the vertices.

   e. Find the profit at each vertex.

   f. How many batches of each size of cake should the bakery make in one day to maximize profit? What is the maximum profit?

Discovering Advanced Algebra More Practice Your Skills
©2004 Key Curriculum Press

Lesson 7.1 • Polynomial Degree and Finite Differences

Name _____ Period _____ Date _____

1. Identify the degree of each polynomial.

    a. $3x^4 - 2x^3 + 3x^2 - x + 7$ **b.** $x^5 - 1$

    c. $0.2x - 1.5x^2 + 3.2x^3$ **d.** $250 - 16x^2 + 20x$

    e. $x + x^2 - x^3 + x^4 - x^5$ **f.** $5x^2 - 6x^5 + 2x^6 - 3x^4 + 8$

2. Determine which of the expressions are polynomials. For each
polynomial, state its degree and write it in general form. If it is
not a polynomial, explain why not.

    a. $1 + x^2 - x^3$ **b.** $0.2x^3 + 0.5x^4 + 0.6x^2$

    c. $x - \dfrac{1}{x^2}$ **d.** 25

    e. $-\dfrac{2}{3}x^2 + \dfrac{3}{5}x^3 + \dfrac{5}{12} + \dfrac{5}{8}x$ **f.** $\sqrt{x} + 3x^2 + 5$

3. For the data set below, find each set of common differences until the
common differences are constant. State the degree of polynomial that
models the data.

x	-3	-2	-1	0	1	2	3
y	22	22	14	4	-2	2	22

4. The figures below show why the numbers in the sequence 1, 3, 6,
10, . . . are called *triangular numbers*.

    a. Complete the table.

n	1	2	3	4	5	6	7
nth triangular number	1	3	6	10			

    b. Calculate the finite differences for the completed table.

    c. What is the degree of the polynomial function that you would use
        to model this data set?

    d. Write a polynomial function t that gives the nth triangular number
        as a function of n. (*Hint:* Create and solve a system of equations to
        find the coefficients.)

Lesson 7.2 • Equivalent Quadratic Forms

Name _____ Period _____ Date _____

1. Identify each quadratic function as being in general form, vertex form, factored form, or none of these forms. Give all answers that apply.

   a. $y = 3x^2 - 4x + 5$

   b. $y = (x - 2.5)^2 + 7.5$

   c. $y = -0.5(x + 3)^2$

   d. $y = 2(x - 8)(x + 6)$

   e. $y = -1.5x(x - 2)$

   f. $y = x^2 - 7$

2. Convert each quadratic function to general form.

   a. $y = 2x(x - 5)$

   b. $y = (x - 3)^2$

   c. $y = 1.5(x + 2)^2 - 3$

   d. $y = 2(x - 5)(x + 7)$

   e. $y = -5(x + 3)(x - 2) - 30$

   f. $y = 3(x - 1.5)^2 - 10$

   g. $y = -\frac{1}{2}(x - 6)^2$

   h. $y = \frac{2}{3} - \left(x - \frac{1}{2}\right)^2$

   i. $y = -2.5(x - 4)(x + 6)$

3. Find the vertex of the graph of each quadratic function.

   a. $y = -x^2$

   b. $y = x^2 + 5$

   c. $y = (x - 4)^2$

   d. $y = (x + 3)^2 - 5$

   e. $y = -(x - 1)^2 + 6$

   f. $y = 10 - (x + 6)^2$

   g. $y = 6.5 + 0.5(x + 4)^2$

   h. $y = -2\left(x - \frac{2}{3}\right)^2 + \frac{1}{4}$

   i. $y = \frac{1}{2}\left(x + \frac{5}{6}\right)^2 - \frac{7}{12}$

4. Find the zeros of each quadratic function.

   a. $y = (x + 5)(x - 3)$

   b. $y = -2(x - 1)(x + 6)$

   c. $y = 0.5x(x - 5)$

   d. $y = (x - 7.5)^2$

   e. $y = -0.2(x + 3.6)(x - 4.8)$

   f. $y = 6\left(x + \frac{2}{3}\right)\left(x - \frac{1}{2}\right)$

5. Consider this table of values generated by a quadratic function.

x	−3	−2.5	−2	−1.5	−1	−0.5	0
y	−0.5	−3	−4.5	−5	−4.5	−3	−0.5

   a. What is the line of symmetry for the graph of the quadratic function?

   b. Identify the vertex of the graph of this quadratic function, and determine whether it is a maximum or a minimum.

   c. Use the table of values to write the quadratic function in vertex form.

Discovering Advanced Algebra More Practice Your Skills
©2004 Key Curriculum Press

Lesson 7.3 • Completing the Square

Name _____   Period _____   Date _____

1. Factor each quadratic expression.

   a. $x^2 + 10x + 25$

   b. $x^2 - 22x + 121$

   c. $x^2 - x + \dfrac{1}{4}$

   d. $4x^2 - 20x + 25$

   e. $0.04x^2 + 1.8x + 20.25$

   f. $9x^2 - 24xy + 16y^2$

2. What value is required to complete the square?

   a. $x^2 + 6x +$ _____

   b. $x^2 - 18x +$ _____

   c. $x^2 - 5x +$ _____

   d. $x^2 + 11x +$ _____

   e. $x^2 - 0.8x +$ _____

   f. $x^2 + 4.3x +$ _____

3. Convert each quadratic function to vertex form.

   a. $y = x^2 - 8x + 14$

   b. $y = x^2 + 14x + 50$

   c. $y = x^2 + 5x + 8$

   d. $y = x^2 - 11x + 28$

   e. $y = 5x^2 - 10x - 3$

   f. $y = 2x^2 + 5x$

4. Find the vertex of the graph of each quadratic function, and state whether the vertex is a maximum or a minimum.

   a. $y = x^2 - 6x + 11$

   b. $y = (x - 2)(x + 6)$

   c. $y = -3x^2 + 12x + 17$

   d. $y = -3.5x^2 - 7x$

   e. $y = x^2 + 9x - 10$

   f. $y = -0.5x^2 + 2.5x + 8$

5. Rewrite each expression in the form $ax^2 + bx + c$, and then identify the coefficients a, b, and c.

   a. $5 + x + 4x^2$

   b. $2x - 5x^2$

   c. $-6 + 3x^2 + 6x + 8$

   d. $-2x(x - 8)$

   e. $25 - x^2$

   f. $(2x - 3)(x + 5)$

6. A ball is thrown up and off the roof of a 75 m tall building with an initial velocity of 14.7 m/s.

   a. Let t represent the time in seconds and h represent the height of the ball in meters. Write an equation that models the height of the ball.

   b. At what time does the ball reach maximum height? What is the ball's maximum height?

   c. At what time or times is the ball 30 m above the ground?

   d. At what time does the ball hit the ground?

Lesson 7.4 • The Quadratic Formula

Name _____ Period _____ Date _____

1. Solve.

   a. $(x - 5)^2 = 49$ **b.** $(x + 12)^2 = 169$ **c.** $(x + 1.3)^2 = 20.25$

   d. $(x - 2.8)^2 = 39.69$ **e.** $\left(x - \dfrac{2}{3}\right)^2 = \dfrac{25}{81}$ **f.** $\left(x + \dfrac{5}{6}\right)^2 = \dfrac{49}{144}$

2. Evaluate each expression. Round your answers to the nearest thousandth.

   a. $\dfrac{-6 + \sqrt{6^2 - 4(1)(-5)}}{2(1)}$ **b.** $\dfrac{4 - \sqrt{(-4)^2 - 4(2)(1)}}{2(2)}$

   c. $\dfrac{5 + \sqrt{(-5)^2 - 4(4)(-3)}}{2(4)}$ **d.** $\dfrac{-10 - \sqrt{10^2 - 4(2)(5)}}{2(2)}$

3. Solve by any method. Give your answers in exact form.

   a. $x^2 + 3x - 10 = 0$ **b.** $x^2 + 12x + 35 = 0$ **c.** $2x^2 - 5x = 12$

   d. $x^2 + 3x - 5 = 0$ **e.** $12x^2 - 11x - 5 = 0$ **f.** $25x^2 - 49 = 0$

   g. $2x^2 - 4x - 7 = 0$ **h.** $4x^2 + 7x - 1 = 0$ **i.** $6x^2 + 19x = 7$

   j. $x^2 = 5.8x$ **k.** $x^2 - 48 = 0$ **l.** $x^2 - 9.6x + 23.04 = 0$

4. Write each equation in factored form, $y = a(x - r_1)(x - r_2)$, where r_1 and r_2 are the roots of the equation.

   a. $y = x^2 - 7x + 12$ **b.** $y = x^2 + 5x - 24$ **c.** $y = x^2 - 7x - 8$

   d. $y = 2x^2 - 8x + 6$ **e.** $y = 4x^2 + 2x - 2$ **f.** $y = 5x^2 + 19x + 12$

5. Write a quadratic function in general form that satisfies the given conditions.

   a. $a = 1$; x-intercepts of graph are 6 and 9.

   b. $a = -1$; x-intercepts of graph are -4 and -2.

   c. $a = 2$; x-intercepts of graph are -7 and 5.

   d. x-intercepts of graph are 8 and -3; y-intercept is -12.

   e. x-intercepts of graph are 0 and 13; graph contains point (2, 22).

   f. x-intercept of graph is 4.8; y-intercept is -5.76.

Discovering Advanced Algebra More Practice Your Skills
©2004 Key Curriculum Press

Lesson 7.5 • Complex Numbers

Name _____ Period _____ Date _____

1. Add, subtract, or multiply.

   a. $(4 - 5i) + (6 + 2i)$

   b. $(-5 + 6i) - (1 - i)$

   c. $4(2 - 5i)$

   d. $\left(\frac{3}{5} - \frac{1}{10}i\right) - \left(\frac{7}{10} - \frac{4}{5}i\right)$

   e. $(-2.4 - 5.6i) + (5.9 + 1.8i)$

   f. $-4i(-6 + i)$

   g. $(3 - 2i)(3 + 2i)$

   h. $(2.5 + 1.5i)(3.4 - 0.6i)$

2. Find the conjugate of each complex number.

   a. $3 - 2i$

   b. $5 - 4i$

   c. -2

   d. $7i$

   e. $\frac{1}{3} + \frac{5}{6}i$

   f. $-3.25 + 4.82i$

3. Rewrite each quotient in the form $a + bi$.

   a. $\dfrac{2}{3 + i}$

   b. $\dfrac{1 + i}{1 - i}$

   c. $\dfrac{3 + 2i}{4 - i}$

   d. $\dfrac{3i}{2 + i}$

   e. $\dfrac{3 + 5i}{6i}$

   f. $\dfrac{4 + 5i}{2 - 3i}$

4. Solve each equation. Label each solution as real, imaginary, and/or complex.

   a. $x^2 - 2x + 5 = 0$

   b. $x^2 + x - 3 = 0$

   c. $2x^2 - 3x + 1 = 0$

   d. $x^2 + 7 = 0$

   e. $3x^2 + 2x + 4 = 0$

   f. $x(x - 5) = 1$

   g. $x^2 + x + 1 = 0$

   h. $4x^2 + 9 = 0$

   i. $(x + 7)(x - 3) = 5 - 2x$

5. Write a quadratic function in general form that has the given zeros and leading coefficient of 1.

   a. $x = -4, x = 7$

   b. $x = 11i, x = -11i$

   c. $x = -2 + 3i, x = -2 - 3i$

Lesson 7.6 • Factoring Polynomials

Name _____ Period _____ Date _____

1. Without graphing, find the x-intercepts and the y-intercept for the graph of each equation.

   a. $y = (x + 6)(x - 5)$ b. $y = -(x - 8)^2$ c. $y = 2(x + 1)(x - 1)$

   d. $y = 3(x + 4)(x + 2)$ e. $y = -(x + 2)(x - 1)(x - 6)$ f. $y = 0.75x(x - 2)(x + 6)$

2. Write the factored form of the quadratic function. Don't forget the vertical scale factor.

   a.   b.

   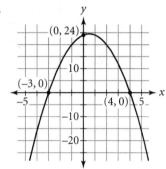   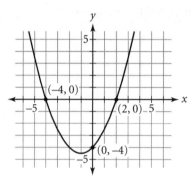

3. Convert each polynomial function to general form.

   a. $y = (x + 5)(x - 3)$ b. $y = -2(x - 2.5)(x + 2.5)$ c. $y = x(x - 1)(x + 5)$

   d. $y = -0.5(x + 3)^2$ e. $y = -x(x + 12)(x - 12)$ f. $y = 0.8(x + 4)(x - 6)$

4. Write each polynomial as a product of factors.

   a. $2x^2 + 4x - 30$ b. $x^2 - 14x + 49$ c. $x^3 - 3x^2 + 2x$

   d. $2x^2 + 3x - 5$ e. $x^2 - 169$ f. $x^2 + 169$

   g. $x^2 - 15$ h. $x^2 + 15$ i. $x^4 - 10x^2 + 9$

   j. $12x^2 - 5x - 3$ k. $x^3 + 5x^2 - 17x - 21$ l. $3x^3 + 3x^2 - 30x + 24$

5. Sketch a graph for each situation if possible.

   a. A quadratic function with two real zeros, whose graph has the line $x = 2$ as its axis of symmetry

   b. A quadratic function with no real zeros, whose graph has a negative y-intercept

   c. A cubic function with three real zeros, whose graph has a positive y-intercept

   d. A cubic function with two real zeros, whose graph has a negative y-intercept

Discovering Advanced Algebra More Practice Your Skills
©2004 Key Curriculum Press

Lesson 7.7 • Higher-Degree Polynomials

Name _____ Period _____ Date _____

1. Refer to these two graphs of polynomial functions.

i.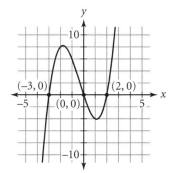

ii.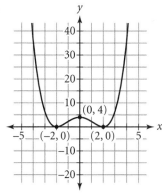

a. Identify the zeros of each function.

b. Find the y-intercept of each graph.

c. Identify the lowest possible degree of each function.

d. Write the factored form for each polynomial function. Check your work by graphing on your calculator.

2. Write a polynomial function with the given features.

a. A quadratic function whose graph has only one x-intercept, -4, and whose y-intercept is -8

b. A cubic function with leading coefficient -1 whose graph has x-intercepts 0 and 5, where $x = 5$ is a double root

c. A quadratic function whose graph has vertex $(3, -8)$, which is a minimum, and two x-intercepts, one of which is 5

d. A fourth-degree polynomial function with two double roots, 0 and 2, and whose graph contains the point $(1, -1)$

3. Write the lowest-degree polynomial function that has the given set of zeros and whose graph has the given y-intercept. Write each polynomial function in factored form. Give the degree of each function.

a. Zeros: $x = -3$, $x = 5$; y-intercept: -30

b. Zeros: $x = -2$ (triple root); y-intercept: -8

c. Zeros: $x = -2$, $x = 1$, $x = 3$; y-intercept: 3

d. Zeros: $x = \pm 2i$, $x = -2$ (double root), $x = 5$; y-intercept: 80

Lesson 7.8 • More About Finding Solutions

Name _____ Period _____ Date _____

1. Divide.

   a. $x - 2 \overline{) 3x^3 - 8x^2 - 11x + 30}$

   b. $x - 4 \overline{) x^4 - 13x^2 - 48}$

   c. $\dfrac{32x^5 - 1}{2x - 1}$

2. Varsha started out dividing two polynomials by synthetic division this way:

   $$-3 \rvert -3 \quad -5 \quad 0 \quad -35 \quad 7$$

   a. Identify the dividend and divisor.

   b. Write the numbers that will appear in the second line of the synthetic division.

   c. Write the numbers that will appear in the last line of the synthetic division.

   d. Write the quotient and remainder for this division.

3. In each division problem, use the polynomial that defines P as the dividend and the quotient that defines D as the divisor. Write the result of the division in the form $P(x) = D(x) \cdot Q(x) + R$, where the polynomial that defines Q is the quotient and R is an integer remainder. (It is not necessary to write the remainder if $R = 0$.)

   a. $P(x) = x^2 + 8x - 9; D(x) = x + 9$

   b. $P(x) = 2x^2 - 9x + 2; D(x) = x - 5$

   c. $P(x) = 2x^3 - 5x^2 + 8x - 5; D(x) = x - 1$

   d. $P(x) = 6x^3 - 5x^2 + 16x - 8; D(x) = 3x - 1$

4. Make a list of the possible rational roots of each equation.

   a. $x^3 + x^2 - 10x + 8 = 0$

   b. $2x^3 - 3x^2 - 17x + 30 = 0$

5. Find all the zeros of each polynomial function. Then write the function in factored form.

   a. $y = x^3 - 6x^2 + 5x + 12$

   b. $y = x^3 - 5x^2 + 9x - 45$

   c. $y = 6x^3 + 17x^2 + 6x - 8$

   d. $y = x^4 - 21x^2 - 100$

Discovering Advanced Algebra More Practice Your Skills
©2004 Key Curriculum Press

Lesson 8.1 • Graphing Parametric Equations

Name _____ Period _____ Date _____

1. Create a table for each pair of parametric equations with the given values of t.

   a. $x = t + 5$
   $y = t^2 + 1$
   $t = \{-2, -1, 0, 1, 2\}$

   b. $x = |t - 3|$
   $y = |t + 3|$
   $t = \{-4, -2, 0, 2, 4\}$

   c. $x = t^2 - 1$
   $y = t^2 + t$
   $t = \{-4, 0, 2, 4, 8\}$

2. Find four points on the graph of each pair of parametric equations. (Choose your own values of t.)

   a. $x = 3t - 1, y = 2t + 1$ b. $x = |t|, y = |t - 5|$ c. $x = \sqrt{t}, y = t^2$

   d. $x = t^2 + 2, y = t^2 - t$ e. $x = -\sqrt{t}, y = 2 - t^2$ f. $x = t^3 - 4, y = (t + 2)^2$

3. Without actually graphing, determine whether the graph of each pair of parametric equations is a line, parabola, or semicircle. (Assume that the t-interval allows the complete graph to be traced.)

   a. $x = t, y = t^2 + 3t + 1$ b. $x = t, y = \sqrt{4 - t^2}$ c. $x = t, y = 2t - 1$

   d. $x = t + 1, y = t - 1$ e. $x = t - 3, y = t^2 + 1$ f. $x = -t, y = -\sqrt{1 - t^2}$

4. Roz and Diana are both taking walks. These parametric equations simulate their motion, with x and y measured in meters and t measured in seconds.

Roz	Diana
$x = 1.6t$	$x = 380$
$y = 250$	$y = 1.1t$

   a. Graph the motion of the walkers for $0 \leq t \leq 500$ in a window that shows all of their walk.

   b. Give a real-world meaning for each value in the equations.

   c. Where do the two paths meet?

   d. Do Roz and Diana meet? How do you know?

Lesson 8.2 • Converting from Parametric to Nonparametric Equations

Name _____ Period _____ Date _____

1. Solve each equation for t.

    a. $x = 2t - 1$ **b.** $y = t^3$ **c.** $x = t^2 + 1$

    d. $y = \sqrt{9 - t^2}$ **e.** $y = t^2 + 2t + 1$ **f.** $x = 5 - t^3$

2. Write a single equation using only x and y that is equivalent to each pair of parametric equations. (Each equation should express y in terms of x.)

    a. $x = t$ **b.** $x = 2t + 5$ **c.** $x = t^2$

        $y = 3t^2 + 2t - 1$ $y = t - 3$ $y = 3t - 2$

    d. $x = t + 7$ **e.** $x = t - 4$ **f.** $x = t - 3$

        $y = t + 5$ $y = -3(t - 6)^2$ $y = |2t - 5|$

    g. $x = \dfrac{t + 1}{2}$ **h.** $x = \dfrac{t - 1}{4}$ **i.** $x = \dfrac{t^2 + 4}{2}$

        $y = \dfrac{t - 2}{3}$ $y = \sqrt[3]{t - 1}$ $y = 3t - 5$

3. This table gives x- and y-values for several values of t.

    a. Write an equation for x in terms of t.

    b. Write an equation for y in terms of t.

    c. Eliminate the parameter and combine the two equations.

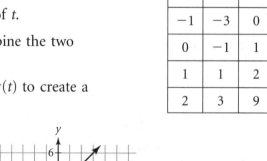

t	x	y
-2	-5	-7
-1	-3	0
0	-1	1
1	1	2
2	3	9

4. Use the graphs of $x = f(t)$ and $y = g(t)$ to create a graph of y as a function of x.

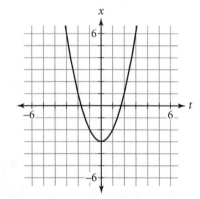
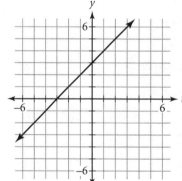

Discovering Advanced Algebra More Practice Your Skills
©2004 Key Curriculum Press

Lesson 8.3 • Right Triangle Trigonometry

Name _____ Period _____ Date _____

1. For each of the following right triangles, find the values of sin A, cos A, tan A and sin B, cos B, tan B. (Write your answers as fractions in lowest terms.)

a.

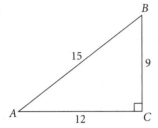

b.

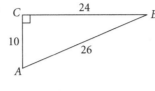

2. Draw a right triangle for each problem. Label the sides and angles with the given measures, then solve to find the unknown value. Round your answers to the nearest tenth.

a. $\cos 27° = \dfrac{r}{8.5}$ b. $\tan^{-1}\left(\dfrac{9}{10}\right) = S$

c. $\sin 81° = \dfrac{w+2}{12.8}$ d. $\cos 52° = \dfrac{z-3}{z}$

3. For each triangle, write an equation to calculate the labeled measure. Then solve the equation.

a.

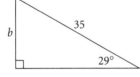

b.

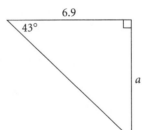

c.

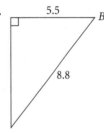

4. Draw a pair of horizontal and vertical lines, and label the four directions with N, E, S, and W for north, east, south, and west. Sketch the path of a plane flying on a bearing of 74°.

   a. Find the measure of the angle between the plane's path and the horizontal axis.

   b. Write a pair of parametric equations that describe the plane's position after flying for t hours along this path at 375 mi/h.

   c. If the plane flies at 375 mi/h for 2.5 h, how far east and how far north will it have traveled?

Lesson 8.4 • Using Trigonometry to Set a Course

Name _____ Period _____ Date _____

1. Find the bearing of each direction. Give the signs of the component vectors for each bearing.

   a. 37° east of north   b. 37° north of east   c. 54° west of north

   d. 54° north of west   e. 42° west of south   f. 42° south of west

   g. 11° south of east   h. 11° east of south   i. 11° north of west

2. Draw a compass rose and vector with magnitude v for each bearing. Find the angle the vector makes with the x-axis.

   a. 192°   b. 111°   c. 63°   d. 336°

3. Imagine that a car is moving with the given speed at the given angle. Write parametric equations for the horizontal and vertical components of each motion in terms of the sine and cosine of an acute angle.

   a. 15 units/s at 42° from the x-axis

   b. 32 units/s at 27° from the y-axis

   c. 12 units/s on a bearing of 122°

   d. 21 units/s on a bearing of 303°

   e. 39 units/s on a bearing of 245°

4. Give the bearing for the actual course flown by each airplane and the actual distance that the airplane will travel in 3 hours. (Round angles to the nearest tenth of a degree and distances to the nearest mile.)

   a. The pilot heads the plane due east at 300 mi/h. There is a constant 25 mi/h wind blowing from the south.

   b. The pilot heads the plane due west at 250 mi/h. There is a constant 30 mi/h wind blowing from the south.

   c. The pilot heads the plane due west at 328 mi/h. There is a constant 22 mi/h wind blowing from the north.

   d. The pilot heads the plane due east at 404 mi/h. There is a constant 32.5 mi/h wind blowing from the north.

Lesson 8.5 • Projectile Motion

Name _____ Period _____ Date _____

1. The height of a falling object is given by the equation $y = -16t^2 + s_0$, where t is the time (measured in seconds) and s_0 is the initial height of the object (measured in feet). Find the height of an object dropped from the indicated height after the indicated amount of time.

   a. $s_0 = 65, t = 1.5$ b. $s_0 = 100, t = 2.4$ c. $s_0 = 426, t = 4.7$

2. Find all positive solutions for each equation. Round to the nearest hundredth.

   a. $-16t^2 + 11.25 = 0$ b. $-4.9t^2 + 20.4 = 0$

   c. $-4.9t^2 + 9.8t + 30 = 0$ d. $-16t^2 + 32t + 55 = 0$

   e. $-16t^2 + 100t \sin 30° + 5 = 0$ f. $-4.9t^2 + 35t \sin 28° + 1.5 = 0$

3. Write parametric equations to simulate each motion.

   a. A ball rolls off the edge of a table that is 1.75 m high at an initial velocity of 2.3 m/s.

   b. A baseball is hit with an initial velocity of 132 ft/s at an angle of 28°. The bat contacts the ball at a height of 3.5 ft above the ground.

   c. A golfer swings a club with a loft of 42° and an initial velocity of 128 ft/s on level ground.

4. In each situation described in Exercise 3, how long will it take the ball to hit the ground? Round to the nearest hundredth.

5. Hayden rolls a ball off the edge of the roof of a 75 ft tall building at an initial velocity of 6.5 ft/s.

   a. Write parametric equations to simulate this motion.

   b. What equation can you solve to determine when the ball hits the ground?

   c. How long after it rolls off the roof does the ball hit the ground? (Round to the nearest hundredth.)

   d. How far from the base of the building (directly below the spot where the ball rolls off the roof) does the ball hit the ground? (Round to the nearest hundredth.)

Lesson 8.6 • The Law of Sines

Name _____ Period _____ Date _____

1. Solve each equation for b. Give an exact answer and an approximate answer. Round to the nearest tenth.

   a. $\dfrac{\sin 75°}{9} = \dfrac{\sin 20°}{b}$

   b. $\dfrac{\sin 95°}{b} = \dfrac{\sin 45°}{6.2}$

   c. $\dfrac{\sin 32.4°}{12} = \dfrac{\sin 120.5°}{b}$

2. Find the unknown angle measures and side lengths. Round to the nearest tenth.

   a.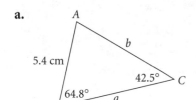

   b.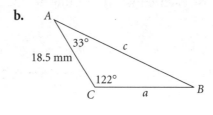

3. Determine the number of triangles with the given parts. (Do not find the missing side lengths and angle measures.)

   a. $A = 32°$, $B = 48°$, $a = 13.5$ cm

   b. $A = 103°$, $a = 8.5$ cm, $b = 6.7$ cm

   c. $B = 50°$, $b = 22.6$ cm, $c = 27.2$ cm

   d. $A = 68°$, $a = 25$ cm, $c = 32$ cm

4. A ship is sailing due east. At a certain point, the captain observes a lighthouse at a bearing of 32°. After the ship sails 28.0 km farther, the bearing of the same lighthouse from the ship is 310°.

   a. Draw a diagram to illustrate this situation. Let A be the point where the first lighthouse observation is made, B be the point where the second observation is made, and C be the location of the lighthouse. Show the given bearings and distance on your diagram.

   b. Find the measure of each angle in $\triangle ABC$.

   c. Use the Law of Sines to write equations for the distance between the lighthouse and the ship at the time of the first observation and at the time of the second observation.

   d. Find the distance between the lighthouse and the ship at the time of the first observation.

   e. Find the distance between the lighthouse and the ship at the time of the second observation.

Discovering Advanced Algebra More Practice Your Skills
©2004 Key Curriculum Press

Lesson 8.7 • The Law of Cosines

Name _____ Period _____ Date _____

1. Solve for b and C. Assume b is positive.

   a. $b^2 = 14^2 + 29^2 - 2(14)(29)\cos 123.5°$

   b. $3.8^2 = 4.0^2 + 5.1^2 - 2(4.0)(5.1)\cos C$

2. Use the given values to write an equation for the unknown measure.
   Then solve the equation. Give an exact answer and an approximate
   answer. Round to the nearest tenth.

   a. $b = 9$
      $c = 12$
      $A = 110°$
      $a = $ _____

   b. $a = 5$
      $b = 3$
      $c = 4$
      $A = $ _____

   c. $a = 3.5$
      $b = 6.9$
      $C = 82.5°$
      $c = $ _____

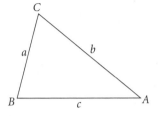

3. State whether you would use the Law of Sines or the Law of Cosines
   to solve each problem.

   a. Given the measures of two angles of a triangle and the length of
      one of the sides that is not between them, find the length of one of
      the other two sides.

   b. Given the lengths of all three sides of a triangle, find the measure
      of the smallest angle.

   c. Given the lengths of two sides and the measure of the angle
      between them, find the length of the third side.

   d. Given the measures of two angles of a triangle and the length of the
      side between them, find the length of one of the other two sides.

4. Find unknown angle measures and side lengths. Round to the nearest
   tenth.

   a.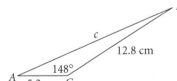

   b.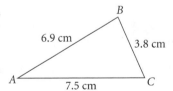

5. Use the Law of Cosines to solve each problem. Round to the nearest
   tenth.

   a. What is the length of the longer diagonal of a parallelogram with
      sides of length 13.2 cm and 18.9 cm and with a pair of opposite
      angles that each measure 47°?

   b. What is the measure of the largest angle of a triangular garden
      whose sides measure 12.5 ft, 19.8 ft, and 15.7 ft?

   c. Sara and Geoff hiked 2.5 mi on a bearing of 58°. Then they turned
      and hiked an additional 3.1 mi on a bearing of 158°. How far were
      they from their starting point?

Lesson 9.1 • Using the Distance Formula

Name _____ Period _____ Date _____

1. Find the exact distance between each pair of points.

   a. (0, 0) and (5, 12)   **b.** (0, 0) and $(-7, 24)$ **c.** (2, 8) and (6, 11)

   d. $(-2, 5)$ and (2, 7)   **e.** $(4, -7)$ and $(8, -15)$ **f.** $(-8, -13)$ and $(1, -10)$

   g. (3a, 8) and $(-2a, 5)$ **h.** $(-2c, 4d)$ and $(c, -3d)$ **i.** $\left(\dfrac{1}{2}, \dfrac{1}{4}\right)$ and $\left(-\dfrac{1}{2}, \dfrac{9}{4}\right)$

2. Find the possible values of x or y.

   a. The distance between the points $(-4, 6)$ and $(2, y)$ is 10 units.

   b. The distance between the points $(4, -5)$ and $(x, 3)$ is 11 units.

3. For each set of vertices, identify the shortest side of $\triangle ABC$ and find the perimeter of the triangle. Round your answers to the nearest hundredth.

   a. $A(0, 0)$, $B(-5, 5)$, $C(4, 6)$ **b.** $A(-1, -3)$, $B(2, 4)$, $C(5, 7)$

4. Find an equation of the locus of points that satisfies the given condition.

   a. The points that are 5 units from $(-2, 3)$

   b. The points that are equidistant from (0, 0) and (2, 5)

   c. The points that are twice as far from $(-9, 0)$ as they are from (0, 0)

5. The perpendicular bisector of a segment is the locus of all points that are equidistant from the endpoints of the segment. Consider $\triangle ABC$ with vertices $A(-3, 0)$, $B(2, 5)$, and $C(5, 0)$.

   a. Draw $\triangle ABC$ on a coordinate plane.

   b. Find equations of the perpendicular bisectors of the three sides.

   c. Use your equations from 5b to find the point where the three perpendicular bisectors coincide. Call this point D.

   d. Find the distance from D to each vertex of the triangle. What do you notice?

Discovering Advanced Algebra More Practice Your Skills
©2004 Key Curriculum Press

Lesson 9.2 • Circles and Ellipses

Name _____ Period _____ Date _____

1. Find the center and radius of each circle.

   a. $x^2 + y^2 = 16$

   b. $(x - 3)^2 + y^2 = 100$

   c. $(x - 0.5)^2 + (y + 0.5)^2 = 0.25$

   d. $\left(x + \frac{1}{3}\right)^2 + \left(y - \frac{2}{3}\right)^2 = \frac{25}{49}$

   e. $x = \cos t + 1$
      $y = \sin t$

   f. $x = 10 \cos t - 8$
      $y = 10 \sin t - 6$

2. Find the center, horizontal scale factor, and vertical scale factor for each ellipse.

   a. $\left(\dfrac{x}{3}\right)^2 + \left(\dfrac{y}{5}\right)^2 = 1$

   b. $\left(\dfrac{x - 2}{4}\right)^2 + \left(\dfrac{y}{2}\right)^2 = 1$

   c. $\dfrac{(x + 5)^2}{9} + \dfrac{(y - 4)^2}{25} = 1$

   d. $x = 7 \cos t$
      $y = 4 \sin t$

   e. $x = 2 \cos t - 3$
      $y = 5 \sin t$

   f. $x = \cos t$
      $y = 2 \sin t + 6$

3. Sketch each ellipse in Exercise 2. Give the exact coordinates of the endpoints of the major and minor axes, and the foci.

4. Write parametric equations for the graph of each equation. Identify each graph as a circle or an ellipse.

   a. $x^2 + y^2 = 121$

   b. $(x - 5)^2 + (y + 2)^2 = 1$

   c. $\dfrac{x^2}{4} + \dfrac{y^2}{16} = 1$

   d. $\left(\dfrac{x + 2}{5}\right)^2 + \left(\dfrac{y - 1}{5}\right)^2 = 1$

   e. $\left(\dfrac{x - 4}{7}\right)^2 + \left(\dfrac{y - 6}{9}\right)^2 = 1$

   f. $\left(\dfrac{x}{8.5}\right)^2 + \left(\dfrac{y + 2}{10.5}\right)^2 = 1$

5. Write an equation in standard form for each graph.

   a.
   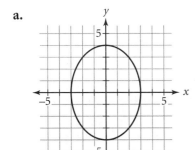

   b.
   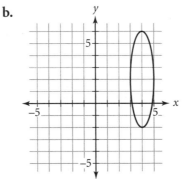

   c.
   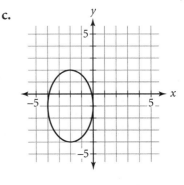

6. The entrance to a tunnel over a one-way road is half an ellipse with height 12 ft and width 36 ft.

   a. Sketch the tunnel entrance on a coordinate plane. Place the center of the ellipse at the origin. Label the endpoints of the major and minor axes of the ellipse that appear in your sketch with their coordinates.

   b. Write the equation in standard form for the complete ellipse.

   c. Will a truck that is 12 ft wide and 10 ft high clear the tunnel? Explain your reasoning.

Lesson 9.3 • Parabolas

Name _____ Period _____ Date _____

1. For each parabola described, use the information given to find the location of the missing feature. It may help to draw a sketch.

   a. If the vertex is $(0, 0)$ and the focus is $(4, 0)$, where is the directrix?

   b. If the focus is $(0, 7)$ and the directrix is $y = -3$, where is the vertex?

   c. If the vertex is $(5, 0)$ and the directrix is $x = 1.5$, where is the focus?

   d. If the focus is $(2, -3)$ and the directrix is $x = -1$, where is the vertex?

   e. If the focus is $(-3, -1)$ and the vertex is $(-3, 4)$, where is the directrix?

2. Find the vertex of each parabola and state whether the parabola opens upward, downward, to the right, or to the left. Also give the equation of the axis of symmetry.

   a. $y = x^2 - 5$

   b. $y = -4x^2$

   c. $x = 2y^2 + 1$

   d. $x = -(y - 3)^2$

   e. $y + 2 = -(x + 1)^2$

   f. $\left(\dfrac{y - 4}{2}\right)^2 = \dfrac{x + 5}{4}$

3. Write parametric equations for each parabola.

   a. $y = x^2 + 4$

   b. $x = y^2 - 3$

   c. $y = (x - 2)^2 + 5$

   d. $\dfrac{x - 5}{6} = \left(\dfrac{y + 3}{2}\right)^2$

   e. $\dfrac{y + 1.5}{2} = (x + 3.5)^2$

   f. $x = 2(y + 1)^2 + 4$

4. Write an equation in standard form for each parabola. Then write parametric equations for the parabola.

   a.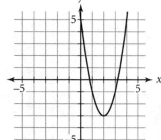

   b.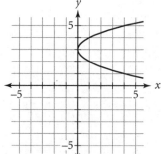

   c.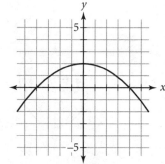

5. Solve each problem by finding the coordinates of the vertex of a parabola.

   a. What are the dimensions of a rectangular field of maximum area that can be enclosed with 76 ft of fencing? What is the area of the field?

   b. The height of a projectile shot straight upward with an initial velocity of 50 m/s from the top of a 60 m tall building is given by the function $h = -4.9t^2 + 50t + 60$. How long does it take the projectile to reach its maximum height? What is the maximum height? Round your answers to the nearest tenth.

Discovering Advanced Algebra More Practice Your Skills
©2004 Key Curriculum Press

Lesson 9.4 • Hyperbolas

Name _____ Period _____ Date _____

1. Write an equation in standard form for each graph.

a.
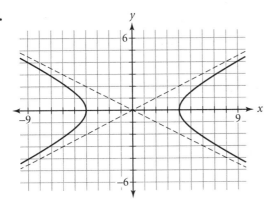

b.
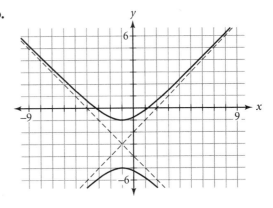

c.
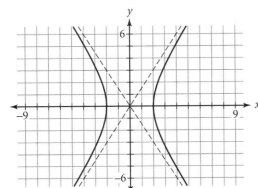

d.
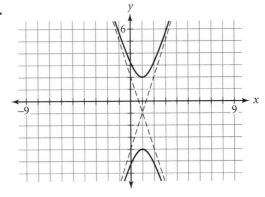

2. Write parametric equations for each graph in Exercise 1.

3. Sketch each hyperbola on your paper. Include the asymptotes and the foci. Write the equations of the asymptotes, and give the exact coordinates of the vertices and the foci.

a. $x^2 - y^2 = 1$

b. $y^2 - x^2 = 1$

c. $\left(\dfrac{x-1}{3}\right)^2 - \left(\dfrac{y}{5}\right)^2 = 1$

d. $x = \dfrac{1}{\cos t}$
   $y = 3\tan t$

e. $x = 2\tan t - 3$
   $y = \dfrac{4}{\cos t} + 1$

f. $\dfrac{(x+4)^2}{16} - \dfrac{(y+2)^2}{25} = 1$

4. Identify each path described as an ellipse or a hyperbola. Then write the equation in standard form for each path.

a. A point moves in a plane so that the difference of its distances from the points (0, 5) and (0, −5) is always 8 units.

b. A point moves in a plane so that the sum of its distances from the points (−4, 0) and (4, 0) is always 10 units.

c. A point moves in a plane so that the difference of its distances from the points (2, −3) and (−6, −3) is always 6 units.

Lesson 9.5 • The General Quadratic

Name _____   **Period** _____   **Date** _____

1. Complete the square for each expression. Then write the expression in factored form.

   a. $x^2 + 8x$ **b.** $y^2 - 22y$ **c.** $x^2 - 5x$

   d. $y^2 + y$ **e.** $x^2 + 6.2x$ **f.** $y^2 - 2.7y$

2. Identify the graph of each equation as a circle, an ellipse, a parabola, or a hyperbola. Then rewrite each equation in the general quadratic form, $Ax^2 + Bxy + Cy^2 + Dx + Ey + F = 0$. (Include all coefficients.)

   a. $(x - 7)^2 + (y + 2)^2 = 25$ **b.** $(y + 6)^2 = 4(x - 5)$ **c.** $\dfrac{(x - 2)^2}{4} + \dfrac{(y + 3)^2}{9} = 1$

   d. $\dfrac{(x - 4)^2}{9} - \dfrac{(y - 3)^2}{16} = 1$ **e.** $0.5(x - 4)^2 = 6.5(y - 2)$ **f.** $\dfrac{(y - 3)^2}{25} = 1 - \dfrac{(x + 4)^2}{25}$

3. Convert each equation to the standard form of a conic section.

   a. $y^2 + 6y - x = 0$ **b.** $x^2 - y^2 - 6x + 13 = 0$

   c. $9x^2 - 4y^2 - 72x + 8y + 104 = 0$ **d.** $x^2 + y^2 - 12x + 10y + 45 = 0$

   e. $16x^2 + 25y^2 - 32x + 100y - 284 = 0$ **f.** $4x^2 - 8x + 2y + 11 = 0$

4. Name the shape described by each equation in Exercise 3. Give the vertex of each parabola and the center of each circle, ellipse, and hyperbola.

5. Solve each equation for y by using the quadratic formula.

   a. $4x^2 + 9y^2 - 36 = 0$ **b.** $x^2 + 2x - 4y^2 + 20 = 0$

   c. $3x^2 + 4y^2 - 5y + 2 = 0$ **d.** $2x^2 + 3y^2 - 6x + 8y - 1 = 0$

6. Solve each system of equations algebraically, using the substitution method or the elimination method.

   a. $\begin{cases} y = x^2 - 4 \\ y = 2x - 1 \end{cases}$ **b.** $\begin{cases} y = -x^2 + 5 \\ y = (x - 3)^2 \end{cases}$ **c.** $\begin{cases} 2x^2 + 3y^2 - 5 = 0 \\ 3x^2 - 4y^2 + 1 = 0 \end{cases}$

Discovering Advanced Algebra More Practice Your Skills
©2004 Key Curriculum Press

Lesson 9.6 • Introduction to Rational Functions

Name _____ Period _____ Date _____

1. Write an equation and graph each transformation of the parent function $f(x) = \frac{1}{x}$.

   a. Translate the graph left 4 units.

   b. Translate the graph up 6 units and left 1 unit.

   c. Translate the graph left 3 units and down 4 units.

   d. Vertically stretch the graph by a scale factor of 3.

   e. Horizontally stretch the graph by a scale factor of 2 and translate it down 2 units.

   f. Reflect the graph across the y-axis.

2. Write equations for the asymptotes of each hyperbola.

   a. $y = \frac{2}{x}$

   b. $y = \frac{1}{x + 3}$

   c. $y = \frac{1}{x} - 4$

   d. $y = -\frac{3}{x}$

   e. $y = \frac{1}{x} + 5$

   f. $y = \frac{1}{x - 2} - 6$

   g. $y = -\frac{1}{x} + 2$

   h. $y = \frac{4}{x + 2} - 1$

   i. $y = 5 + \frac{2}{x - 4}$

3. Solve.

   a. $\frac{6}{x - 5} = -2$

   b. $\frac{1}{x - 2} = 6$

   c. $\frac{4}{2x + 5} = -\frac{1}{2}$

   d. $8 = \frac{x + 4}{x - 3}$

   e. $-2 = \frac{2x + 14}{x - 1}$

   f. $0.4 = \frac{5x - 4}{10x - 3}$

4. Write a rational equation that can be used to solve each problem, using x as the variable. Then use your equation to solve the problem.

   a. A baseball player got 34 hits in his first 142 at-bats this season. How many consecutive hits must he get to bring his batting average up to .280?

   b. How much water must be added to 120 mL of a 35% alcohol solution to dilute it to a 25% alcohol solution?

Lesson 9.7 • Graphs of Rational Functions

Name _____ Period _____ Date _____

1. Rewrite each rational expression in factored form.

   a. $\dfrac{x^2 - 5x - 6}{x^2 - 25}$

   b. $\dfrac{2x^2 + 3x - 2}{3x^2 - 5x - 2}$

   c. $\dfrac{x^2 - 16}{6x^2 - 7x - 3}$

   d. $\dfrac{4x^3 - 25x}{x^2 - 14x + 48}$

   e. $\dfrac{x^3 + 5x^2 - 24x}{x^2 + 6x + 9}$

   f. $\dfrac{9x^2 - 1}{2x^3 - x^2 - 3x}$

2. Rewrite each expression in rational form (as the quotient of two polynomials).

   a. $\dfrac{2}{x} + 3$

   b. $1 + \dfrac{1}{x - 2}$

   c. $4 + \dfrac{2x - 7}{x + 5}$

   d. $\dfrac{3x + 4}{2x - 3} - 1$

   e. $\dfrac{5x - 7}{x + 3} - 4$

   f. $-6 + \dfrac{10x - 3}{3x - 5}$

3. Find all vertical and horizontal asymptotes of the graph of each rational function.

   a. $f(x) = \dfrac{x}{x - 1}$

   b. $f(x) = \dfrac{2x + 5}{x + 3}$

   c. $f(x) = -\dfrac{1}{x^2}$

   d. $f(x) = \dfrac{3}{(x - 2)^2}$

   e. $f(x) = \dfrac{x^2 + x + 1}{x^2 - 4}$

   f. $f(x) = \dfrac{x - 3}{x^2 + 6x + 8}$

4. Find all vertical and slant asymptotes of the graph of each rational function.

   a. $f(x) = \dfrac{x^2}{x - 1}$

   b. $f(x) = \dfrac{x^2 + 1}{x}$

   c. $f(x) = \dfrac{x^2 + x - 1}{x - 1}$

   d. $f(x) = \dfrac{2x^2 - 5}{x + 3}$

   e. $f(x) = \dfrac{x^3}{x^2 - 4}$

   f. $f(x) = \dfrac{9 - x^2}{2 + x}$

5. Give the coordinates of all holes in the graph of each rational function.

   a. $f(x) = \dfrac{x - 3}{3 - x}$

   b. $f(x) = \dfrac{x + 5}{x + 5}$

   c. $f(x) = \dfrac{2x + 6}{x + 3}$

   d. $f(x) = \dfrac{x^2 - 4}{x + 2}$

   e. $f(x) = \dfrac{x^2 - 3x - 10}{x + 2}$

   f. $f(x) = \dfrac{x^3 + x^2 - x - 1}{x + 1}$

Discovering Advanced Algebra More Practice Your Skills
©2004 Key Curriculum Press

Lesson 9.8 • Operations with Rational Expressions

Name _____ Period _____ Date _____

1. Factor each expression completely and reduce common factors.

a. $\dfrac{x^2 - 4x}{x^2 - x - 12}$

b. $\dfrac{x^2 - 49}{x^2 + 14x + 49}$

c. $\dfrac{2x^2 - 10x}{3x^2 - 11x - 20}$

d. $\dfrac{4x^2 - 1}{6x^2 - x - 2}$

e. $\dfrac{9x^2 - 30x + 25}{9x^2 - 12x - 5}$

f. $\dfrac{4x^2 + 21x + 5}{5x^2 + 23x - 10}$

2. Find the least common denominator for each pair of rational expressions.

a. $\dfrac{3}{(x + 4)(x + 2)}, \dfrac{5}{(x + 4)(x - 5)}$

b. $\dfrac{3x}{x^2 - 16}, \dfrac{2x}{x^2 + 5x + 4}$

c. $\dfrac{2x - 1}{x^2 - 4x + 4}, \dfrac{3x^2}{x^2 - 6x + 8}$

d. $\dfrac{x + 3}{x^2 - 7x - 8}, \dfrac{x - 5}{2x^2 + x}$

3. Add, subtract, multiply, or divide as indicated. Reduce any common factors.

a. $\dfrac{3}{(x + 2)(x - 1)} + \dfrac{5}{(x + 1)(x - 1)}$

b. $\dfrac{4}{x^2 - 49} - \dfrac{x}{(x + 7)(x - 1)}$

c. $\dfrac{x + 4}{x^2 - 3x + 2} \cdot \dfrac{x^2 + 3x - 10}{x^2 - 16}$

d. $\dfrac{x^2}{x^2 - 5x + 6} + \dfrac{2x}{x^2 - 9}$

e. $\dfrac{x + 5}{x - 5} \div \dfrac{x^2 - 25}{x}$

f. $\dfrac{x^2 + 2x - 15}{2x^2 + 9x - 5} \cdot \dfrac{4x^2 - 1}{2x^2 - 5x - 3}$

g. $\dfrac{9x^2 + 6x}{2x - 1} \div \dfrac{6x^2 + x - 2}{4x^2 - 4x + 1}$

h. $\dfrac{x + 9}{x^2 - 9x} - \dfrac{x - 9}{x^2 + 9x}$

4. Rewrite each fraction as a single rational expression.

a. $\dfrac{\dfrac{2x - 1}{x^2}}{\dfrac{2x^2 + 3x - 2}{x}}$

b. $\dfrac{\dfrac{x^2 - 9}{x^2 - 2x - 3}}{\dfrac{x^2 + 6x + 9}{x + 1}}$

c. $\dfrac{\dfrac{1}{x - 2} + \dfrac{1}{x + 2}}{\dfrac{x}{x + 2} - \dfrac{x}{x - 2}}$

Lesson 10.1 • Defining the Circular Functions

Name _____ Period _____ Date _____

1. Find the exact value of each expression.

    a. $\sin 60°$ **b.** $\cos 45°$ **c.** $\sin 150°$ **d.** $\cos 225°$

    e. $\sin(-30°)$ **f.** $\sin(-120°)$ **g.** $\sin 315°$ **h.** $\cos 240°$

    i. $\sin(-240°)$ **j.** $\sin 90°$ **k.** $\sin 270°$ **l.** $\sin 360°$

2. Use your calculator to find each value, approximated to four decimal places. Name each reference angle.

    a. $\sin 37°$ **b.** $\cos 115°$ **c.** $\sin(-21°)$ **d.** $\cos 195°$

    e. $\sin 91°$ **f.** $\sin 203°$ **g.** $\cos 349°$ **h.** $\sin(-310°)$

    i. $\cos(-94°)$ **j.** $\cos(-282°)$ **k.** $\sin 234°$ **l.** $\cos(-196°)$

3. Determine whether each function whose graph is shown below is periodic or not periodic. For each periodic function, identify the period.

    a.   **b.**

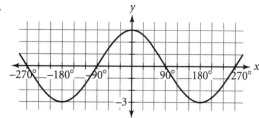 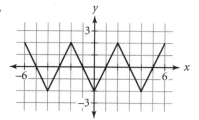

    c.

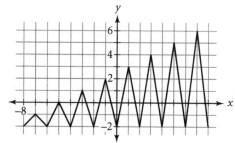

4. Identify an angle θ that is coterminal with the given angle. Use domain $0° \leq \theta \leq 360°$.

    a. $-42°$ **b.** $415°$ **c.** $913°$ **d.** $-166°$

    e. $-294°$ **f.** $1129°$ **g.** $-498°$ **h.** $1735°$

5. Find $\sin \theta$ and $\cos \theta$ for each angle in standard position described.

    a. The terminal side of angle θ passes through the point $(5, 12)$.

    b. The terminal side of angle θ passes through the point $(-4, 5)$.

    c. The terminal side of angle θ passes through the point $(-1, -6)$.

Discovering Advanced Algebra More Practice Your Skills
©2004 Key Curriculum Press

Lesson 10.2 • Radian Measure and Arc Length

Name _____ Period _____ Date _____

1. Convert between radians and degrees. Give exact answers.

   a. $\dfrac{5\pi}{4}$

   b. $15°$

   c. $330°$

   d. $-\dfrac{2\pi}{3}$

   e. $-140°$

   f. $72°$

   g. $-\dfrac{13\pi}{4}$

   h. $780°$

   i. $\dfrac{7\pi}{10}$

   j. $-\dfrac{11\pi}{6}$

   k. $1260°$

   l. $\dfrac{17\pi}{15}$

2. Find the intercepted arc length for each central angle.

   a. $r = 8$ and $\theta = \dfrac{5\pi}{4}$

   b. $r = 5.4$ and $\theta = 2.5$

   c. $d = 10$ and $\theta = \dfrac{5\pi}{6}$

   d. $d = 3$ and $\theta = \dfrac{\pi}{12}$

3. Solve for θ.

   a. $\sin\theta = \dfrac{\sqrt{3}}{2}$ and $90° \le \theta \le 180°$

   b. $\cos\theta = -\dfrac{\sqrt{2}}{2}$ and $180° \le \theta \le 270°$

   c. $\sin\theta = -\dfrac{1}{2}$ and $270° \le \theta \le 360°$

   d. $\sin\theta = -1$ and $0° \le \theta \le 360°$

   e. $\cos\theta = \dfrac{1}{2}$ and $\pi \le \theta \le 2\pi$

   f. $\dfrac{\sin\theta}{\cos\theta} = 1$ and $\pi \le \theta \le \dfrac{3\pi}{2}$

   g. $\cos\theta = -\dfrac{\sqrt{3}}{2}$ and $\pi \le \theta \le 2\pi$

   h. $\dfrac{\sin\theta}{\cos\theta} = \dfrac{1}{\sqrt{3}}$ and $0 \le \theta \le \dfrac{\pi}{2}$

4. The minute hand on a watch is 85 mm long. Round your answers in 4a and b to the nearest tenth, and in 4c to the nearest thousandth.

   a. What is the distance the tip of the minute hand travels, in mm?

   b. At what speed is the tip moving, in mm/min?

   c. What is the angular speed of the tip in radians/min?

Lesson 10.3 • Graphing Trigonometric Functions

Name _____ Period _____ Date _____

1. Find the period of each function in radians.

    a. $y = \sin 3x$ **b.** $y = \cos 2x$ **c.** $y = \tan 4x$

    d. $y = \sin\left(\frac{1}{2}x\right)$ **e.** $y = \cos\left(\frac{1}{3}x\right)$ **f.** $y = \tan\left(\frac{1}{4}x\right)$

    g. $y = -\sin\left(\frac{2}{3}x\right)$ **h.** $y = -\tan\left(\frac{3}{2}x\right)$ **i.** $y = \cos\left(\frac{3}{5}x\right)$

2. Find the maximum and minimum values (if any) of each function. Also give the amplitude, if any.

    a. $y = \sin x$ **b.** $y = \cos\left(x - \frac{\pi}{8}\right)$ **c.** $y = \tan x$

    d. $y = \sin 2x$ **e.** $y = \cos x + 2$ **f.** $y = \tan x - 3$

    g. $y = 3\sin x$ **h.** $y = -0.5\cos 3x$ **i.** $y = 2.5\cos(0.5x) + 1.5$

3. Write an equation for each sinusoid as a transformation of the graph of either $y = \sin x$ or $y = \cos x$. More than one answer is possible.

    a.

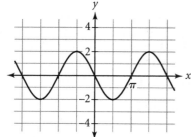

    b.

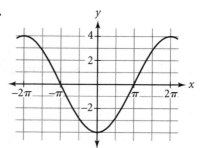

    c.

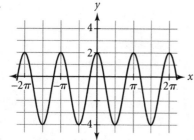

    d.

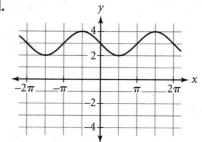

4. Sketch the graph of each function for the interval $0 \le \theta \le 2\pi$.

    a. $y = 2\sin x + 1$ **b.** $y = \sin\left(x - \frac{\pi}{3}\right)$ **c.** $y = -\tan x$

    d. $y = -\cos\left(\frac{x}{2}\right)$ **e.** $y = \tan\left(x + \frac{\pi}{2}\right)$ **f.** $y = 3\cos\left(x + \frac{\pi}{4}\right)$

5. Write an equation for each sinusoid with the given characteristics.

    a. A cosine curve with amplitude 2.5, period 2π, and phase shift $\frac{\pi}{4}$

    b. A sine function with minimum value 2, maximum value 8, and one cycle starting at $x = 0$ and ending at $x = \frac{3\pi}{2}$

Discovering Advanced Algebra More Practice Your Skills
©2004 Key Curriculum Press

Lesson 10.4 • Inverses of Trigonometric Functions

Name _____ Period _____ Date _____

1. Find the principal value of each expression to the nearest tenth of a degree and then to the nearest hundredth of a radian.

   a. $\sin^{-1} 0.5976$

   b. $\cos^{-1}(-0.9523)$

   c. $\cos^{-1}(-0.0315)$

   d. $\sin^{-1} 0.4$

   e. $\cos^{-1}(0.8665)$

   f. $\sin^{-1}(-0.6789)$

2. Find all four values of x between -2π and 2π that satisfy each equation.

   a. $\sin x = \sin \dfrac{2\pi}{3}$

   b. $\cos x = \cos \dfrac{5\pi}{12}$

   c. $\sin x = \sin 1.25$

   d. $\cos x = \cos 0.73$

   e. $\cos x = \cos \dfrac{3\pi}{5}$

   f. $\sin x = \sin \dfrac{9\pi}{7}$

   g. $\sin x = \sin 2.45$

   h. $\cos x = \cos 5.21$

   i. $\sin x = \sin\left(-\dfrac{5\pi}{6}\right)$

3. Find values of x approximate to three decimal places that satisfy these criteria.

   a. Find the first two positive solutions of $\sin x = 0.9827$.

   b. Find the first two positive solutions of $\cos x = 0.7205$.

   c. Find the two solutions closest to zero of $\cos x = -0.8406$.

   d. Find the first two positive solutions of $\tan x = 2$.

4. Find each angle described to the nearest tenth of a degree.

   a. The largest angle of a triangle with sides of lengths 13.52 m, 20.15 m, and 17.26 m

   b. The smallest angle of a triangle with sides of lengths 32 cm, 31 cm, and 36 cm

   c. The smallest angle of a triangle in which two of the sides have lengths 13 cm and 28 cm, and in which the angle opposite the 28 cm side measures 110°

Lesson 10.5 • Modeling with Trigonometric Equations

Name _____   Period _____   Date _____

1. Find all solutions for $0 \leq x < 2\pi$. Give exact values in radians.

   a. $\sin x = 1$
   b. $\cos x = -0.5$
   c. $\sin 2x = -1$

   d. $\cos x = 0$
   e. $\cos 3x = 0.5$
   f. $2\sin\left(\frac{1}{2}x\right) = 1$

   g. $\sin\frac{x}{2} = \frac{\sqrt{2}}{2}$
   h. $\cos\left(x - \frac{\pi}{4}\right) = \frac{\sqrt{3}}{2}$
   i. $\cos\frac{x}{2} = -\frac{\sqrt{2}}{2}$

2. Find all solutions for $0 \leq x < 2\pi$, rounded to the nearest hundredth.

   a. $\sin(x - 1.2) = 0.82$
   b. $3\cos(x + 0.4) = 2.6$

   c. $5 + 0.5\sin 2x = 4.7$
   d. $13.5 - 15\sin(x - 2.8) = 10$

3. Consider the graph of the function

   $$h = 8.5 + 5\sin\left(\frac{2\pi(t - 4)}{7}\right)$$

   a. What is the vertical translation?
   b. What is the average value?

   c. What is the vertical stretch factor?
   d. What is the minimum value?

   e. What is the maximum value?
   f. What is the amplitude?

   g. What is the horizontal stretch factor?
   h. What is the period?

   i. What is the horizontal translation?
   j. What is the phase shift?

4. The number of hours of daylight on any day of the year in Philadelphia, Pennsylvania, is modeled using the equation

   $$y = 12 + 2.4\sin\left(\frac{2\pi(x - 80)}{365}\right)$$

   where x represents the day number (with January 1 as day 1). This equation assumes a 365-day year (not a leap year).

   a. Find the number of hours of daylight in Philadelphia on day 172, the longest day of the year (the summer solstice).

   b. Find the day numbers of the two days when the number of hours of daylight is closest to 13.

   c. Find the calendar dates for the summer solstice and for the two day numbers you found in 4b.

Discovering Advanced Algebra More Practice Your Skills
©2004 Key Curriculum Press

Lesson 10.6 • Fundamental Trigonometric Identities

Name _____ Period _____ Date _____

1. Evaluate. Give exact values.

a. $\tan\dfrac{\pi}{3}$

b. $\cot\dfrac{5\pi}{6}$

c. $\sec\dfrac{\pi}{4}$

d. $\csc\dfrac{4\pi}{3}$

e. $\cot\pi$

f. $\sec\dfrac{11\pi}{6}$

g. $\csc\dfrac{9\pi}{2}$

h. $\cot\dfrac{5\pi}{3}$

i. $\csc\dfrac{7\pi}{6}$

2. Find another function that has the same graph as each function below.
(More than one answer is possible.)

a. $y = \tan(x + \pi)$

b. $y = \sin(x - 2\pi)$

c. $y = \sin\left(x + \dfrac{\pi}{2}\right)$

d. $y = \tan\left(x + \dfrac{\pi}{2}\right)$

e. $y = \sec(x - \pi)$

f. $y = \cot(-x)$

g. $y = \cos\left(x - \dfrac{3\pi}{2}\right)$

h. $y = \sec(-x)$

i. $y = -\csc(x - 2\pi)$

3. Use trigonometric identities to rewrite each expression in a simplified
form containing only sines and cosines, or as a single number.

a. $\tan\theta + \sec\theta$

b. $\left(\sec^2\theta - \tan^2\theta\right)\cos^2\theta$

c. $\cot\theta\sin^2\theta - \tan\theta\cos^2\theta$

d. $2\tan^2\theta\csc^2\theta\cos^3\theta$

e. $(\csc\theta + \cot\theta)(\csc\theta - \cot\theta)$

f. $\left(\dfrac{1}{\sec\theta} - \dfrac{1}{\csc\theta}\right)(\tan\theta\cos\theta)$

4. Determine whether each equation is an identity or not an identity.

a. $\sin(A + \pi) = \cos A$

b. $\tan\left(A - \dfrac{\pi}{2}\right) = -\cot A$

c. $(\cos A + \sin A)(\cos A - \sin A) = 1$

d. $(\sec A + \tan A)(\sec A - \tan A) = 1$

e. $\csc^2 A = \cot A(\tan A + \cot A)$

f. $(1 + \sin A)(1 - \sin A) = -\cos^2 A$

g. $\sec A \cot A = \csc A$

h. $(1 + \tan A)(1 - \tan A) = \sec^2 A$

Lesson 10.7 • Combining Trigonometric Functions

Name _____ Period _____ Date _____

1. Use a graph or substitute values of A and B to decide whether each equation is an identity or not an identity.

   a. $\cos 2A = 1 - 2\sin^2 A$

   b. $\sin(A - B) = \sin A - \sin B$

   c. $\sin(2\pi - A) = \sin A$

   d. $\cos(A + \pi) = -\cos A$

   e. $\cos 2A = 2\cos^2 A - 1$

   f. $\sin\left(A - \dfrac{\pi}{2}\right) = \cos A$

   g. $\tan 2A = \dfrac{\sin 2A}{\cos 2A}$

   h. $\cos(A - B) = \cos A \cos B - \sin A \sin B$

2. Use identities from this lesson to derive an identity for $\sin 3A$ in terms of $\sin A$ and $\cos A$. Show the steps you used to derive the identity.

3. Rewrite each expression as a single sine or cosine.

   a. $\sin 3.2 \cos 2.5 - \cos 3.2 \sin 2.5$

   b. $2 \sin 4.8 \cos 4.8$

   c. $\cos 0.9 \cos 1.7 - \sin 0.9 \sin 1.7$

   d. $\sin 7.2 \cos 2.8 + \cos 7.2 \sin 2.8$

   e. $\cos^2 0.8 - \sin^2 0.8$

   f. $\cos 0.6 \cos 2.1 + \sin 0.6 \sin 2.1$

4. Use a sum or difference identity to find the exact value of each expression.

   a. $\sin \dfrac{5\pi}{12}$

   b. $\cos \dfrac{\pi}{12}$

   c. $\sin\left(-\dfrac{\pi}{12}\right)$

   d. $\cos \dfrac{17\pi}{12}$

   e. $\sin 105°$

   f. $\cos 285°$

5. Find the exact values of $\sin 2x$, $\cos 2x$, and $\tan 2x$ for each set of conditions.

   a. $\sin x = \dfrac{3}{5}, 0 \le x \le \dfrac{\pi}{2}$

   b. $\cos x = -\dfrac{5}{13}, \dfrac{\pi}{2} \le x \le \pi$

   c. $\sin x = -\dfrac{1}{4}, \pi \le x \le \dfrac{3\pi}{2}$

   d. $\cos x = \dfrac{2}{5}, \dfrac{3\pi}{2} \le x \le 2\pi$

   e. $\sec x = -\dfrac{10}{3}, \dfrac{\pi}{2} \le x \le \pi$

   f. $\csc x = \sqrt{5}, \dfrac{\pi}{2} \le x \le \pi$

Discovering Advanced Algebra More Practice Your Skills
©2004 Key Curriculum Press

Lesson 11.1 • Arithmetic Series

Name _____ Period _____ Date _____

1. List the first six terms of each arithmetic sequence and identify the common difference.

   a. $u_1 = 5$
      $u_n = u_{n-1} + 6$ where $n \geq 2$

   b. $u_1 = 7.8$
      $u_n = u_{n-1} - 2.3$ where $n \geq 2$

   c. $u_3 = -4.6$
      $u_n = u_{n-1} + 1.8$ where $n \geq 2$

   d. $u_5 = -22$
      $u_n = u_{n-1} - 7$ where $n \geq 2$

2. Write each expression as a sum of terms and calculate the sum.

   a. $\displaystyle\sum_{n=1}^{3} (n - 5)$

   b. $\displaystyle\sum_{n=1}^{5} n^3$

   c. $\displaystyle\sum_{n=1}^{4} (3n - 7)$

   d. $\displaystyle\sum_{n=1}^{5} \left(2n^2 + 5\right)$

   e. $\displaystyle\sum_{n=2}^{7} (1.5n + 4)$

   f. $\displaystyle\sum_{n=3}^{6} \left(\frac{1}{2}n^3 - n^2 + 1\right)$

3. Find the indicated values.

   a. u_{20} if $u_n = 2.5n - 10$

   b. u_{31} if $u_n = -8n + 5.5$

   c. u_{18} if $u_n = \frac{2}{3}n + \frac{3}{4}$

   d. S_{10} if $u_n = 3n - 6$

   e. S_{14} if $u_n = 0.8n + 9.5$

   f. S_{75} if $u_n = 3n$

   g. $\displaystyle\sum_{n=1}^{12} (15 - 7n)$

   h. $\displaystyle\sum_{n=1}^{100} (9n - 81)$

   i. $\displaystyle\sum_{n=51}^{100} (9n - 81)$

4. There are 22 rows of seats in a high school auditorium. There are 17 seats in the front row, and each of the other rows has two more seats than the row directly in front of it.

   a. List the first six terms of the sequence that describes the number of seats in each row, starting with the front row.

   b. Write a recursive formula for this sequence.

   c. Write an explicit formula for the number of seats in row n.

   d. The rows are identified with letters to help people who attend performances in the auditorium find their seats. If the front row is row A, how many seats are there in row M?

   e. How many seats are there in the back row?

   f. How many seats are there in the auditorium?

Lesson 11.2 • Infinite Geometric Series

Name _____ Period _____ Date _____

1. Consider the repeating decimal 0.777..., or $0.\overline{7}$.

   a. Express the decimal as the sum of terms of an infinite geometric sequence.

   b. Identify the first term and common ratio of the sequence.

   c. Express the infinite sum as a ratio of integers in lowest terms.

2. Repeat the three parts of Exercise 1 with the repeating decimal 0.393939..., or $0.\overline{39}$.

3. Repeat the three parts of Exercise 1 with the repeating decimal 0.531531531..., or $0.\overline{531}$.

4. Find the common ratio for each geometric sequence. State whether each series is convergent or not convergent. If the series is convergent, find the sum.

   a. $3 + 4.5 + 6.75 + 10.125 + \cdots$

   b. $5 + 1 + \dfrac{1}{5} + \dfrac{1}{25} + \cdots$

   c. $4 + 3.2 + 2.56 + 2.048 + \cdots$

   d. $10 - 5 + 2.5 - 1.25 + \cdots$

   e. $-2 + 2.2 - 2.42 + 2.662 - \cdots$

   f. $13 + 1.3 + 0.13 + \cdots$

5. Evaluate each sum.

   a. $\displaystyle\sum_{n=1}^{\infty} 4\left(\frac{1}{3}\right)^{n-1}$

   b. $\displaystyle\sum_{n=1}^{\infty} -3\left(\frac{3}{4}\right)^{n-1}$

   c. $\displaystyle\sum_{n=1}^{\infty} 1.1(0.5)^{n-1}$

   d. $\displaystyle\sum_{n=1}^{\infty} 0.2(-0.8)^{n-1}$

   e. $\displaystyle\sum_{n=1}^{\infty} 12\left(-\frac{1}{4}\right)^{n-1}$

   f. $\displaystyle\sum_{n=1}^{\infty} -2.5(-0.1)^{n-1}$

6. The first term of a geometric sequence is 1 and the sum of the series is 3. Find the common ratio and list the first five terms of the sequence.

7. Four consecutive terms of a geometric sequence are 80, 16, 3.2, and 0.64, and the sum of the series is 12,500. Find the first term.

8. The common ratio of a geometric sequence is -0.6 and the sum of the series is 44. Find the first term and list the first four terms of the sequence.

9. A pendulum bob swings through a 50 cm arc on its first swing. For each swing after the first, it swings only 78% as far as on the previous swing. How far will the bob swing altogether before coming to a complete stop?

10. Marcey drops a ball from a height of 12 ft. On each bounce, the ball returns to about $\frac{3}{5}$ of its previous height. What is the total distance the ball travels before coming to rest?

Discovering Advanced Algebra More Practice Your Skills
©2004 Key Curriculum Press

Lesson 11.3 • Partial Sums of Geometric Series

Name _____ **Period** _____ **Date** _____

1. For each partial sum equation, identify the first term, the common ratio, and the number of terms.

a. $\dfrac{15}{1-0.6} - \dfrac{15}{1-0.6} \cdot 0.6^5 = 34.584$

b. $\dfrac{4.5}{1+0.1} - \dfrac{4.5}{1+0.1}(-0.1)^6 \approx 4.090905$

c. $\dfrac{18(1-2.3^{10})}{1-2.3} \approx 57{,}345.9386$

d. $\dfrac{30-0.1171875}{1-0.5} = 59.765625$

2. Consider the geometric sequence $187.5, 75, 30, 12, \ldots$

a. What is the tenth term?

b. Which term is the first one smaller than 1?

c. Find u_9.

d. Find S_9.

3. Find the first term and the common ratio or common difference of each series. Then find the partial sum.

a. $5 + 6.2 + 7.4 + \cdots + 17$

b. $150 - 30 + 6 - 1.2 + \cdots + 0.000384$

c. $\displaystyle\sum_{i=1}^{15} 12.5(1.1)^{n-1}$

d. $\displaystyle\sum_{i=1}^{50}(72 - 3.5n)$

4. Find the missing values.

a. $u_1 = 4,\ r = 3,\ S_{10} = $ _____

b. $u_1 = 2,\ r = 0.8,\ S\_\_\_ = 6.7232$

c. $u_1 = $ _____ $,\ r = 1.1,\ S_6 = 92.58732$

d. $u_1 = 10,\ r = $ _____ $,\ S_{12} = 19.99511719$

5. Suppose that you rent an apartment for \$750 a month. Each year, your landlord raises the rent by 5%.

a. If you make a list of your monthly rent over several years, does this form an arithmetic or geometric sequence? If the sequence is arithmetic, give the common difference; if it is geometric, give the common ratio.

b. To the nearest dollar, what is your monthly rent during the fifth year you rent the apartment?

c. To the nearest ten dollars, what is the total amount of rent that you paid during the first five years you rented the apartment?

Lesson 12.1 • Randomness and Probability

Name _____ Period _____ Date _____

1. A national survey was taken measuring the highest level of educational achievement among adults age 30 and over. Express each probability to the nearest .001.

Highest level of education	Women	Men	Total
8th grade or less	35	46	81
High school graduate	232	305	537
Some college	419	374	793
Bachelor's degree	539	463	1002
Graduate or professional degree	377	382	759
Total	1602	1570	3172

   a. What is the probability that a randomly chosen person from the survey group is a man?

   b. What is the probability that the highest level of education completed by a randomly chosen person from the survey group is a bachelor's degree?

   c. What is the probability that a randomly chosen woman has earned a bachelor's or graduate degree?

   d. What is the probability that a randomly chosen person whose highest level of education is high school is a man?

2. Suppose that a bag contains five green marbles, three blue marbles, six yellow marbles, and four white marbles. Maria shakes up the bag to mix the marbles and then draws one marble out of the bag.

   a. What is the probability that the marble Maria draws is blue?

   b. What is the probability that the marble is white?

   c. What is the probability that the marble is green or yellow?

   d. What is the probability that the marble is neither blue nor yellow?

3. Find each probability.

   a. If a meteorologist says that there is a 35% chance of snow tomorrow, what is the probability that it will not snow?

   b. If you roll a die once, what is the probability that you will get higher than a 2?

Lesson 12.2 • Counting Outcomes and Tree Diagrams

Name _____   Period _____   Date _____

1. Find the probability of each path, a–g, in the tree diagram below.

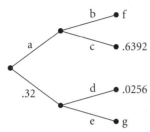

2. Draw a tree diagram that shows all possible equally likely outcomes if a penny is tossed once and then a six-sided die is rolled once. Then use your diagram to find each probability.

  a. What is the probability of tossing a head and rolling a 5?

  b. What is the probability of tossing a tail and rolling an even number?

  c. What is the probability of tossing a head and rolling a number less than 6?

  d. What is the probability of tossing a head and rolling a number greater than 6?

3. Liam draws one playing card from a 52-card deck and places it on the table. Then he draws a second card and places it to the right of the first card.

  a. What is the probability that the first card is a heart and the second card is a diamond?

  b. What is the probability that the first card is a queen and the second card is an 8?

  c. What is the probability that both cards are black?

  d. What is the probability that both cards are aces?

4. Three friends try out for sports teams at their high school. Gladys tries out for the lacrosse team and has a 40% chance of success (making the team). Becky tries out for the synchronized swim team and has a 30% chance of success. Serita tries out for the tennis team and has a 25% chance of success. Use the tree diagram to find each probability.

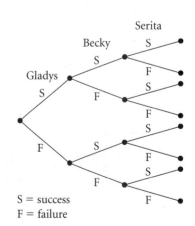

  a. What is the probability that all three girls will make their teams?

  b. What is the probability that none of the girls will be successful?

  c. What is the probability that exactly one of the girls will be successful?

Lesson 12.3 • Mutually Exclusive Events and Venn Diagrams

Name _____ Period _____ Date _____

1. Refer to the Venn diagram, which gives probabilities related to the two events "plays the piano" and "plays the violin." These probabilities apply to the students at Riverway Middle School, which has 800 students.

   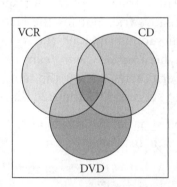

   a. What is the probability that a randomly chosen student at Riverway plays the piano?

   b. What is the probability that a randomly chosen student at Riverway plays neither the piano nor the violin?

   c. How many students at Riverway play both instruments?

   d. How many students play the piano or the violin, but not both instruments?

2. Refer to the Venn diagram in Problem 1. Find the probability of each event indicated. N represents the event that a student plays the piano, and V represents the event that a student plays the violin.

   a. $P(V)$

   b. $P(\text{not } N)$

   c. $P(N \text{ or } V)$

   d. $P(N \text{ and } V)$

   e. $P(\text{not } N \text{ and not } V)$

   f. $P(N \text{ and not } V)$

3. For a class project, Diana surveys 300 students at her high school about the entertainment equipment (CD players, VCRs, and DVD players) they have in their homes. She gathers the following information.

   187 homes had VCRs and 141 homes had DVD players.

   19 homes had no entertainment equipment, while 12 homes had DVD players only.

   81 homes had VCRs and CD players, but not DVD players.

   11 homes had VCRs and DVD players, but not CD players.

   43 homes had CD players and DVD players, but not VCRs.

   a. Complete the Venn diagram of this situation using frequencies.

   b. Complete the Venn diagram using probabilities.

   c. What is the probability that a student's home has a CD player, but neither a VCR nor a DVD player?

   d. What is the probability that a student's home has all three pieces of equipment?

Discovering Advanced Algebra More Practice Your Skills
©2004 Key Curriculum Press

Lesson 12.4 • Random Variables and Expected Value

Name _____ Period _____ Date _____

1. Determine whether each number described below comes from a random variable, a discrete random variable, or a geometric random variable. (List all the terms that apply.)

   a. The number of days of sunshine in Seattle in 2002

   b. The number of times that you get heads if you toss a nickel 100 times

   c. The number of tosses of a nickel that it takes until you get tails

   d. The number of votes cast for a particular candidate in a city council election

   e. The height of a building, measured to the nearest tenth of a meter

   f. The number of times you roll a pair of dice until you get "doubles"

2. You know that 35% of the students in your high school own cell phones. Suppose you stop random students who enter the school on a particular day and ask them if they own cell phones.

   a. What is the probability that the fourth student you ask owns a cell phone?

   b. What is the probability that the fourth student you ask will be the first one who owns a cell phone?

   c. What is the probability that you will find your first cell-phone owner within the first four students you ask?

3. Suppose that you enter a contest that promises to award these prizes:

   1 first prize: $10,000   100 third prizes: $100 each

   50 second prizes: $1,000 each   1000 fourth prizes: $20 each

   One entry is allowed per person, and 50,000 people enter the contest. Let x represent the random variable. Its values are the possible amounts (in dollars) that you may win.

   a. Complete the table to show the probabilities of each possible value of x. (Write each probability as an exact decimal.)

x_i	10,000	1,000	100	20	0
$P(x_i)$					

   b. How many people who enter the contest will not win any prize?

   c. If there is no cost to enter the contest, what are your expected winnings?

   d. If the company running the contest charges $2 for each entry, will the company make a profit or a loss on this contest? How much will the profit or loss be? (Ignore any costs of running the contest.)

Lesson 12.5 • Permutations and Probability

Name _____ Period _____ Date _____

1. Give the number of possible arrangements or selections for each situation.

   a. Arrangements of six poetry books on a shelf

   b. Arrangements of seven students seated in the front row of a classroom

   c. License plates with two letters followed by four digits

   d. License plates with two letters followed by four digits or four digits followed by two letters

   e. Outfits made up of a shirt, a pair of slacks, and a sweater selected from five shirts, four pairs of slacks, and three sweaters

   f. Restaurant meals formed by selecting an appetizer, a salad, a main course, and a dessert from five choices of appetizer, three choices of salad, six choices of main course, and four choices of dessert

   g. Seven-digit telephone numbers, if the first digit cannot be 0

   h. Three-digit integers that are multiples of 5 and have no repeated digits

2. Evaluate each expression. (Some answers will be in terms of n.)

   a. $\dfrac{15!}{14!}$ b. $\dfrac{21!}{19!}$ c. $\dfrac{100!}{97!}$ d. $\dfrac{n!}{(n-2)!}$

   e. $\dfrac{(n+1)!}{(n-1)!}$ f. $_{10}P_2$ g. $_{15}P_4$ h. $_{18}P_3$

   i. $_nP_{n-3}$ j. $_{n+2}P_{n-1}$

3. In Ms. Scarpino's math class, there are six desks in each row. On the first day of the semester, she tells her students that they may sit anywhere they want, but that they must sit in the same row every day.

   a. If the first row is completely filled, in how many different ways can the students who have chosen to sit there be seated?

   b. What is the probability that the students in the front row will be seated in alphabetical order?

   c. What is the probability that among the students in the front row, the tallest student will sit in the chair farthest to the right?

   d. On April Fools' Day, the students came to class and found that two of the desks in the front row were missing. In how many ways could the remaining desks be chosen by the students who usually sit in the front row?

   e. On April Fools' Day, what was the probability that Ricardo, one of the students who usually sits in the front row, was able to get a seat in this row?

Lesson 12.6 • Combinations and Probability

Name _____ Period _____ Date _____

1. Evaluate each expression without using a calculator.

   a. $\dfrac{5!}{3!\,2!}$　　　　b. $\dfrac{8!}{3!\,5!}$　　　　c. $\dfrac{9!}{5!\,4!}$　　　　d. $\dfrac{25!}{0!\,25!}$

2. Evaluate each expression.

   a. $_6C_3$　　　　　　b. $_8C_7$　　　　　　c. $_{24}C_3$　　　　　d. $_{15}C_3$

   e. $_{12}C_6$　　　　　f. $_{20}C_1$　　　　　g. $_{20}C_{19}$　　　　h. $_{20}C_{20}$

   i. $_{20}C_0$　　　　　j. $_{199}C_{199}$　　　　k. $_{199}C_{197}$　　　l. $_{24}C_{12}$

3. Find the number of ways of making each choice.

   a. Selecting three days out of a week

   b. Selecting three days out of a week if exactly two of them must be weekdays

   c. Selecting a 4-member committee from a 20-member club

   d. Selecting a 4-member committee from a 20-member club if the president of the club must be on the committee

   e. Selecting a 4-member committee from a 20-member club if the president of the club cannot be on the committee but the treasurer must be on the committee

   f. Selecting a 4-member committee from a 20-member club if there are 12 women and 8 men in the club and the committee must include 2 men and 2 women

4. There are 10 fourth graders, 12 fifth graders, and 8 sixth graders in a Girl Scout troop. Mrs. Sullivan, the troop leader, needs five girls to serve on the troop's camping committee. To make the selection fair, she lets the girls draw names out of a hat to fill the six places on the committee.

   a. How many different committees are possible?

   b. What is the probability that Lisa Brownell, one of the sixth-grade scouts, will be on the committee?

   c. What is the probability that Lisa and her best friend, Naomi Weiss, will both be on the committee?

   d. What is the probability that all the committee members will be fifth graders?

   e. What is the probability that the committee will be made up of 2 fourth graders, 2 fifth graders, and 1 sixth grader?

Lesson 12.7 • The Binomial Theorem and Pascal's Triangle

Name _____ Period _____ Date _____

1. Expand each binomial, combining like terms when possible.

   a. $(3x - 5y)^2$ b. $(4m + 7n)^2$ c. $(a + 2b)^3$

   d. $\left(\frac{1}{2}y - \frac{1}{3}z\right)^3$ e. $(r - s)^4$ f. $(2c + 5)^4$

2. Find the indicated term of each binomial expansion.

   a. $(2x - y)^3$; 3rd term   b. $(3f + g)^4$; 3rd term   c. $(m - n)^5$; 4th term

   d. $(2a + 3b)^5$; 6th term   e. $(3c + 5d)^6$; 4th term   f. $(m + n)^{20}$; 8th term

3. Find each of the following probabilities for a family with six children. Assume that having a boy and having a girl are equally likely. (Write each probability as a fraction and also as an exact decimal.)

   a. What is the probability that the family will have five girls and one boy?

   b. What is the probability that all of the children will be the same sex?

   c. What is the probability that there will be the same number of children of each sex?

   d. What is the probability that there will be more boys than girls?

   e. What is the probability that there will be at least three girls?

4. The Light and Bright Company manufactures lightbulbs. Over time, the Quality Assurance Department has determined that 2% of all bulbs manufactured in the Light and Bright factory are defective. Determine each probability for a random sample of 20 Light and Bright lightbulbs. (Give your answers as decimals rounded to the nearest thousandth.)

   a. What is the probability that there will be no defective bulbs in the sample?

   b. What is the probability that there will be exactly two defective bulbs in the sample?

   c. What is the probability that there will be no more than two defective bulbs in the sample?

5. Rita and Ron are playing a board game in which each player must roll a pair of dice at the beginning of each turn to determine how many spaces to move on the board. If "doubles" are rolled, the player gets to advance three extra spaces.

   a. What is the probability that Rita will roll doubles on both of her first two turns?

   b. What is the probability that Ron will roll doubles on exactly two of his first five turns?

Discovering Advanced Algebra More Practice Your Skills
©2004 Key Curriculum Press

Lesson 13.1 • Probability Distributions

Name _____ Period _____ Date _____

1. A random-number generator selects a number between 0 and 5 according to the continuous probability distribution shown in the graph.

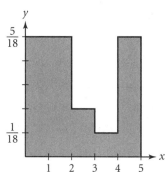

Find the probability that the random number will be

a. Less than 2

b. Between 2 and 4

c. Greater than 3

d. Between 0.5 and 1.5

e. Between 1.5 and 3

f. Between 2.5 and 5

2. The graph represents a probability distribution.

a. Find the value of the y-scale so that the area is 1.

b. Find the probability that a randomly chosen value will be less than 3.

c. Find the probability that a randomly chosen value will be greater than 5.

d. Find the mode.

e. Find the median to the nearest tenth.

f. Find the mean to the nearest tenth.

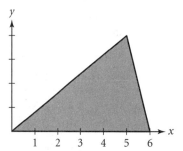

3. The graph represents a continuous probability distribution. The boundary of this graph is an isosceles trapezoid.

a. Find the height of the trapezoid.

b. Find the mean and the median.

c. Does this distribution have a mode? Explain.

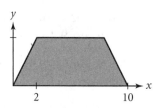

Lesson 13.2 • Normal Distributions

Name _____ **Period** _____ **Date** _____

1. Use the graphs to estimate the mean and standard deviation of each distribution.

   a.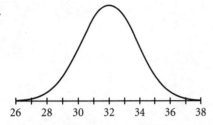

   b.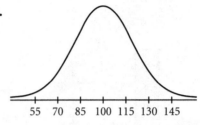

2. Estimate the equation of each graph in Exercise 1.

3. From each equation, find or estimate the mean and standard deviation.

   a. $y = \dfrac{1}{8\sqrt{2\pi}} \cdot \sqrt{e}^{\,-((x-55)/8)^2}$

   b. $y = \dfrac{0.4}{30} \cdot 1.6487^{-((x-325)/30)^2}$

   c. $y = \dfrac{0.4}{0.75} \cdot 0.60653^{-((x-4.8)/0.75)^2}$

   d. $y = 6.132 \cdot 1.0022(1.6487)^{-(x-100)^2}$

4. The weights of 1000 children were recorded on their first birthdays. The weights are normally distributed with mean 10.3 kg and standard deviation 1.6 kg.

   a. What is the probability that a randomly selected child will weigh less than 10 kg?

   b. What is the probability that a randomly selected child will weigh more than 13 kg?

   c. What is the probability that a randomly selected child will weigh between 8.7 kg and 11.9 kg?

   d. What is the probability that a randomly selected child will weigh between 9.5 kg and 11.5 kg?

   e. How many of the 1000 children would you expect to weigh between 9.2 kg and 11.3 kg?

   f. How many of the 1000 children would you expect to weigh between 8.3 kg and 12.3 kg?

   g. How many of the 1000 children would you expect to weigh less than 7.9 kg?

   h. How many of the 1000 children would you expect to weigh more than 8.7 kg?

Lesson 13.3 • z-Values and Confidence Intervals

Name _____ Period _____ Date _____

1. The scores on a standardized test with a maximum score of 150 are normally distributed with mean 108 and standard deviation 11. Find the test score for each of these z-values.

   a. $z = 1$ **b.** $z = -2$ **c.** $z = 0$

   d. $z = 3$ **e.** $z = -1$ **f.** $z = 2$

2. The heights of a group of 500 women are normally distributed with mean 65 inches and standard deviation 2.2 inches. Find the height for each of these z-values to the nearest tenth of an inch.

   a. $z = 2$ **b.** $z = 0.5$ **c.** $z = -1.5$

   d. $z = 1.7$ **e.** $z = -2.3$ **f.** $z = -3.4$

3. For a normal distribution, give the percentage of all data values that fall within each interval.

   a. Within three standard deviations of the mean

   b. Between the mean and one standard deviation above the mean

   c. Between the mean and two standard deviations below the mean

   d. Below the mean or between the mean and 1.645 standard deviations above the mean

4. The mean commuting time for a resident of a certain metropolitan area is 38 minutes, with a standard deviation of 10 minutes. Assume that commuting times for this area are normally distributed.

   a. Find the z-value for a 23-minute commute.

   b. Find the z-value for a 60-minute commute.

   c. What is the probability that a commute for a randomly chosen resident will be between 28 minutes and 58 minutes?

5. A sample has mean 52.6 and standard deviation 6.4. Find each confidence interval. Assume $n = 1$ in each case.

   a. 68% confidence interval   **b.** 90% confidence interval

   c. 95% confidence interval   **d.** 99% confidence interval

   e. 99.5% confidence interval   **f.** 99.9% confidence interval

6. Repeat Exercise 5 assuming $n = 25$.

Lesson 13.4 • The Central Limit Theorem

Name _____ Period _____ Date _____

1. From a population with mean 750 and standard deviation 60, find the probability of

   a. A value of 720 or less

   b. A sample size $n = 4$ with mean 720 or less

   c. A sample size $n = 10$ with mean 720 or less

   d. A sample size $n = 50$ with mean 720 or less

2. For each population and sample, determine what value of sample means would indicate a significant event two standard deviations from the population mean.

   a. $\mu = 100$, $\sigma = 15$, sample size $n = 16$

   b. $\mu = 32.5$, $\sigma = 4$, sample size $n = 25$

   c. $\mu = 250$, $\sigma = 30$, sample size $n = 100$

   d. $\mu = 15.3$, $\sigma = 0.9$, sample size $n = 36$

3. A factory produces and packages breakfast cereal. Its best-selling product is Happy O's, which are sold in 15-ounce (handy size) and 24-ounce (family size) boxes. The weights of the cereal that fills these boxes (net weights) are normally distributed. Because customers might complain if they get less cereal than advertised, the factory supervisor sets the machines so that the mean net weight is 15.4 ounces for the handy size and 24.6 ounces for the family size. The standard deviation is 0.2 ounce for the handy size and 0.32 ounce for the family size. A box is considered underweight if its net weight is less than the advertised weight printed on the box.

   a. What is the probability that a randomly selected handy-size box will be underweight?

   b. What is the probability that a randomly selected family-size box will be underweight?

   c. If a family-size box has net weight greater than 25 ounces, it is considered overstuffed and cannot be sold. What is the probability that a randomly chosen family-size box will be overstuffed?

   d. What is the probability that the mean net weight for a sample of four handy-size boxes will be less than 15 ounces?

   e. What is the probability that the mean net weight for a sample of four family-size boxes will be greater than 25 ounces?

Discovering Advanced Algebra More Practice Your Skills
©2004 Key Curriculum Press

Lesson 13.5 • Bivariate Data and Correlation

Name _____ Period _____ Date _____

1. Complete this table. Then answer 1a–d to calculate the correlation coefficient.

x	y	$x - \bar{x}$	$y - \bar{y}$	$(x - \bar{x})(y - \bar{y})$
2	5			
4	8			
6	10			
8	13			
10	15			
12	18			

   a. What are $\bar{x}$ and $\bar{y}$?

   b. What is the sum of the values for $(x - \bar{x})(y - \bar{y})$?

   c. What are s_x and s_y?

   d. Calculate $r = \dfrac{\sum (x - \bar{x})(y - \bar{y})}{s_x s_y (n - 1)}$.

   e. What does this value of r tell you about the data?

2. In each study described, identify the explanatory and response variables.

   a. The members of a school board investigated the relationship between the number of new housing units built in the school district and the total school enrollment in the following school year.

   b. A pharmaceutical company studied the relationship of the dose of a new medication for lowering cholesterol and the decrease in cholesterol levels among patients taking this medication.

3. For each research finding, decide whether the relationship is causation, correlation, or both. If it is only correlation, name a possible lurking variable that may be the cause of the results.

   a. A pharmaceutical company made a television commercial based on the finding that people who took their daily vitamins lived longer. Do vitamins extend life?

   b. A high school counselor observed that students who take a psychology course are never in the band. Does this mean that students who are interested in psychology have less musical ability than other students do?

Lesson 13.6 • The Least Squares Line

Name _____ Period _____ Date _____

1. The data at right show the population of Lenoxville at five-year intervals. Use the data to calculate each specified value.

   a. $\bar{x}$ b. $\bar{y}$

   c. s_x d. s_y

   e. r

Year x	Population y
1980	15,420
1985	14,860
1990	14,215
1995	13,390
2000	12,625

2. Use the given statistics to calculate the least squares line for each data set described.

   a. $\bar{x} = 20$, $s_x = 3$, $\bar{y} = 72$, $s_y = 6$, $r = .9$

   b. $\bar{x} = 3$, $s_x = 0.25$, $\bar{y} = 6.5$, $s_y = 1.5$, $r = -.8$

   c. $\bar{x} = 28.4$, $s_x = 2.5$, $\bar{y} = 8.3$, $s_y = 0.9$, $r = .98$

   d. $\bar{x} = 1984$, $s_x = 25$, $\bar{y} = 72$, $s_y = 8$, $r = -.95$

3. Use the data from Exercise 1 and the least squares equation $\hat{y} = 295,090 - 141.2x$ to calculate

   a. The residuals

   b. The sum of the residuals

   c. The squares of the residuals

   d. The sum of the squares of the residuals

   e. The root mean square error

4. The table shows the percentage of U.S. television-owning households that had basic cable TV service in certain years.

   Households with Basic Cable TV

Year	1980	1984	1988	1992	1996
Percent	22.6	43.7	53.8	61.5	66.7

   (*The World Almanac and Book of Facts 2000*)

   a. Find the equation of the least squares line for these data using 1970 as the reference year, that is, let $x = 0$ represent the year 1970.

   b. What are the real-world meanings of the slope and the y-intercept?

   c. According to your model, what percentage of households with TV had basic cable service in 1998?

   d. The actual percentage of TV households that had basic cable service in 1998 was 67.4%. How does this compare to your result in 4c? Give a possible explanation for the difference between the actual value and the one predicted by your model.

Lesson 13.7 • Nonlinear Regression

Name _____ Period _____ Date _____

1. The data in the table represent the profit y, in tens of thousands of dollars, made by a small company x years after the company went into business.

x	1	2	3	4	5
y	0.036	0.282	0.945	2.24	4.39

   a. By examining scatter plots created with your calculator, determine which plot appears to be the most linear: (x, y), $(\log x, y)$, $(x, \log y)$, or $(\log x, \log y)$.

   b. Which type of function best models the data: linear, exponential, power, sinusoid, normal, or logistic?

2. Determine whether each data set can best be modeled by a linear, quadratic, or exponential function. Write an equation for the model you choose.

   a.

x	1	2	3	4	5	6
y	1.5	2.2	3.0	4.1	5.8	8.3

   b.

x	1	2	3	4	5
y	5.8	9.1	12.7	16.8	20.3

   c.

x	1	2	3	4	5
y	8	15	22	35	48

3. Solve each equation for $\hat{y}$ and rewrite the function in one of these forms:

   $\hat{y} = a + bx$ $\hat{y} = ab^x + c$

   $\hat{y} = ax^b + c$ $\hat{y} = a + b \log c$

   a. $\hat{y} - 10 = 55 - 8.5 \log x$

   b. $\log(\hat{y} - 10) = 2.35 - 0.375x$

   c. $\hat{y} - 10 = 42.8 - 2.3x$

   d. $\log(\hat{y} - 10) = 2.054 - 0.3726 \log x$

LESSON 0.1 • Pictures, Graphs, and Diagrams

1. a. 2 **b.** $\frac{3}{2}$ **c.** $-\frac{2}{5}$

2. a. $a = 12$ **b.** $b = 36$ **c.** $c = 33$
d. $d = 78$ **e.** $w = 9$ **f.** $x = 280$
g. $y = 72$ **h.** $z = 14$ **i.** $q = 70$

3. a. $\frac{7}{3}$ **b.** $-\frac{5}{2}$ **c.** 1
d. -1 **e.** -2 **f.** $\frac{5}{4}$
g. -3 **h.** $\frac{11}{7}$

4. a. 0.3125 **b.** 0.28 **c.** $0.\overline{4}$
d. $0.\overline{72}$ **e.** $0.\overline{428571}$ **f.** $0.91\overline{6}$
g. 0.675 **h.** $0.98\overline{6}$ **i.** $1.\overline{36}$

5. a. $\frac{7}{8}$ **b.** $\frac{13}{10}$ **c.** $\frac{5}{9}$
d. $\frac{5}{12}$ **e.** $\frac{7}{4}$ **f.** $\frac{2}{11}$
g. $\frac{15}{16}$ **h.** $\frac{47}{99}$ **i.** $\frac{7}{11}$

LESSON 0.2 • Symbolic Representation

1. a. Subtract 7 from both sides.
b. Divide both sides by 8.
c. Add 14 to both sides.
d. Multiply both sides by -11.
e. Subtract 116 from both sides.
f. Divide both sides by -19.

2. a. $a = 27$ **b.** $b = 9$
c. $c = 15$ **d.** $d = -4$
e. $x = 7$ **f.** $y = -26$
g. $z = -4$ **h.** $w = -\frac{27}{8}$, or -3.375
i. $p = -\frac{7}{12}$, or $-0.58\overline{3}$ **j.** $q = \frac{3}{4}$, or 0.75

3. a. $5x - 45$
b. $-21 + 3y$, or $3y - 21$
c. $2z^2 - 16z$
d. $-144q + 12q^2$, or $12q^2 - 144q$
e. $-7y^3 + 21y$
f. $10x^3 - 100x$
g. $6r^2 - 15r$
h. $48s^2 - 30s$
i. $-3y^3 + 5y^2$
j. $16z^3 - 120z$

4. a. 0 **b.** -25 **c.** 36 **d.** 5
e. 26.4 **f.** -18 **g.** 47.2 **h.** 34

LESSON 0.3 • Organizing Information

1. a. $2.6w - 10.4$
b. $-3.5x + 29$, or $29 - 3.5x$
c. $-4.6 - 2y$, or $-2y - 4.6$
d. $21.3 - 3.1z$, or $-3.1z + 21.3$
e. $-37.5r - 18.5$
f. $6.8s - 2.8t + 8.4$
g. $3u - 26$
h. $2v - 4$
i. $14v - 9$
j. $-8z + 12$, or $12 - 8z$

2. a. $p = 3.5$, or $p = \frac{7}{2}$ **b.** $q = -13.3$, or $-\frac{133}{10}$
c. $t = 4.8$, or $t = \frac{24}{5}$ **d.** $u = 17$
e. $m = 13$ **f.** $n = -7$
g. $r = 20$ **h.** $s = -8$
i. $z = -13$ **j.** $w = 33$

3. a. m^{12} **b.** n^{20}
c. t^{21} **d.** r^5
e. s^3 **f.** p^{-10}, or $\frac{1}{p^{10}}$
g. v^{15} **h.** w^{100}
i. $8x^{12}$ **j.** $y^{12}z^{18}$
k. $81a^8b^4$ **l.** $-10x$

4. a. $x^2 + 9x + 20$ **b.** $y^2 - 10y + 21$
c. $z^2 - 5z - 14$ **d.** $r^2 + 3r - 180$
e. $s^2 - 121$ **f.** $t^2 + 8t + 16$
g. $v^2 - 14v + 49$ **h.** $4m^2 - 12m + 9$
i. $25n^2 + 10n + 1$ **j.** $49p^2 - 81$
k. $10y^2 + 37y + 7$ **l.** $6x^2 - 7x - 20$

LESSON 1.1 • Recursively Defined Sequences

1. a. Arithmetic **b.** Geometric
c. Neither **d.** Geometric
e. Geometric **f.** Arithmetic

2. a. $d = 5$ **b.** $r = 0.1$
c. $d = -0.5$ **d.** $r = 2$
e. $r = -0.2$ **f.** $d = 0.01$

3. a. $-18, -12, -6, 0, 6, 12$

b. $0.5, 1.5, 4.5, 13.5, 40.5, 121.5$

c. $35.6, 31.4, 27.2, 23, 18.8, 14.6$

d. $8, -4, 2, -1, 0.5, -0.25$

4. a. $u_1 = -15$ and $u_n = u_{n-1} + 4$ where $n \geq 2$; $u_{10} = 21$

b. $u_1 = 1000$ and $u_n = 0.1u_{n-1}$ where $n \geq 2$; $u_{12} = 0.00000001$

c. $u_1 = 17.25$ and $u_n = u_{n-1} - 2.31$ where $n \geq 2$; $u_{15} = -15.09$

d. $u_1 = 0.3$ and $u_n = -0.1u_{n-1}$ where $n \geq 2$; $u_8 = -0.00000003$

e. $u_1 = 0$ and $u_n = u_{n-1} + \frac{1}{6}$ where $n \geq 2$; $u_{21} = \frac{10}{3}$, or $3\frac{1}{3}$

f. $u_1 = -2$ and $u_n = -2u_{n-1}$ where $n \geq 2$; $u_{15} = -32{,}768$

5. a. Arithmetic; $d = 50$ **b.** Geometric; $r = 1.05$

c. Geometric; $r = 2$ **d.** Arithmetic; $d = -75$

6. $u_1 = 12$ and $u_n = u_{n-1} - 4$ where $n \geq 2$; $u_{42} = -152$

LESSON 1.2 • Modeling Growth and Decay

1. a. 3   **b.** 0.2   **c.** 1.1

d. 0.6   **e.** 3.8   **f.** 0.38

2. a. Growth; 200% increase

b. Decay; 80% decrease

c. Growth; 10% increase

d. Decay; 40% decrease

e. Growth; 280% increase

f. Decay; 62% decrease

3. a. $u_1 = 42$ and $u_n = 3u_{n-1}$ where $n \geq 2$; $u_6 = 10{,}206$

b. $u_1 = 19.2$ and $u_n = 0.2u_{n-1}$ where $n \geq 2$; $u_6 = 0.006144$

c. $u_1 = 90$ and $u_n = 1.1u_{n-1}$ where $n \geq 2$; $u_6 = 144.9459$

d. $u_1 = 1800$ and $u_n = 0.6u_{n-1}$ where $n \geq 2$; $u_6 = 139.968$

e. $u_1 = 11.5$ and $u_n = 3.8u_{n-1}$ where $n \geq 2$; $u_6 = 9112.04432$

f. $u_1 = 375$ and $u_n = 0.38u_{n-1}$ where $n \geq 2$; $u_6 = 2.9713188$

4. a. $(1 + 0.25)x$, or $1.25x$

b. $(1 - 0.19)y$, or $0.81y$

c. $(2 - 0.33)A$, or $1.67A$

d. $(3 + 0.07)B$, or $3.07B$

e. $(1 + 0.085)u_{n-1}$, or $1.085u_{n-1}$

f. $(1 - 0.72)u_{n-1}$, or $0.28u_{n-1}$

g. $(3 - 0.5)u_{n-1}$, or $2.5u_{n-1}$

h. $(1.5 + 0.25)u_{n-1}$, or $1.75u_{n-1}$

5. a. 25.4% increase   **b.** 11.9% decrease

c. 4.5% increase   **d.** 30.7% decrease

e. 22% decrease   **f.** 6% increase

6. a. C   **b.** A   **c.** B

LESSON 1.3 • A First Look at Limits

1. a. $u_1 = 33$, $u_2 = 41$, $u_3 = 49$; arithmetic; increasing

b. $u_1 = 1$, $u_2 = 0.1$, $u_3 = 0.01$; geometric; decreasing

c. $u_1 = 41.1$, $u_2 = 34.2$, $u_3 = 27.3$; arithmetic; decreasing

d. $u_1 = 101$, $u_2 = 102.01$, $u_3 = 103.0301$; geometric; increasing

e. $u_1 = 125$, $u_2 = 50$, $u_3 = 35$; shifted geometric; decreasing

f. $u_1 = 783$, $u_2 = 1281.1$, $u_3 = 2127.87$; shifted geometric; decreasing

2. a. $r = 300$ **b.** $s = 100$ **c.** $t = 0$

d. No solution   **e.** $w = -50$ **f.** $z = 56$

3. a. 0   **b.** 0   **c.** 100

d. 20   **e.** 0   **f.** 100

g. 31.25   **h.** -40

4. a. $u_0 = 0$ and $u_n = 0.8u_{n-1} + 20$ where $n \geq 1$

b. $u_0 = 100$ and $u_n = 1.1u_{n-1} + 50$ where $n \geq 1$

c. $u_0 = 50$ and $u_n = 0.6u_{n-1} + 6$ where $n \geq 1$

d. $u_0 = 40$ and $u_n = 1.6u_{n-1} - 20$ where $n \geq 1$

e. $u_0 = 180$ and $u_n = 0.9u_{n-1} - 18$ where $n \geq 1$

f. $u_0 = 2500$ and $u_n = 0.5u_{n-1} + 30$ where $n \geq 1$

g. $u_0 = 500$ and $u_n = 1.2u_{n-1} + 50$ where $n \geq 1$

h. $u_0 = 90$ and $u_n = 0.8u_{n-1} - 5$ where $n \geq 1$

LESSON 1.4 • Graphing Sequences

1. Sample answers:

a. $(0, 2)$, $(1, 10)$, $(2, 18)$, $(3, 26)$, $(4, 34)$

b. $(0, 10)$, $(1, 1)$, $(2, 0.1)$, $(3, 0.01)$, $(4, 0.001)$

c. $(0, 0)$, $(1, 10)$, $(2, 35)$, $(3, 97.5)$, (253.75)

d. $(0, 150)$, $(1, 110)$, $(2, 78)$, $(3, 52.4)$, $(4, 31.92)$

e. $(0, 60)$, $(1, 60)$, $(2, 60)$, $(3, 60)$, $(4, 60)$

f. $(0, 250)$, $(1, 275)$, $(2, 305)$, $(3, 341)$, $(4, 384.2)$

2. Sample sequences are given.

a. Arithmetic; $u_0 = 30$ and $u_n = u_{n-1} + 5$ where $n \geq 1$

b. Geometric; $u_0 = 80$ and $u_n = 0.75u_{n-1}$ where $n \geq 1$

c. Shifted geometric; $u_0 = 80$ and $u_n = 0.75u_{n-1} + 10$ where $n \geq 1$

d. Geometric; $u_0 = 10$ and $u_n = 1.5u_{n-1}$ where $n \geq 1$

3. a. Arithmetic, linear, decreasing

b. Shifted geometric, nonlinear, decreasing

c. Geometric, nonlinear, increasing

d. Geometric, nonlinear, decreasing

e. Arithmetic, linear, increasing

f. Shifted geometric, nonlinear, increasing

LESSON 1.5 • Loans and Investments

1. a. Investment; principal: $1,000; deposit: $100

b. Loan; principal: $15,500; payment: $475

c. Loan; principal: $130,000; deposit: $1,055

d. Investment; principal: $1,825; deposit: $120

2. a. 4%; annually

b. 6%; semiannually

c. 6.25%, or $6\frac{1}{4}$%; quarterly

d. 7.5%, or $7\frac{1}{2}$%; monthly

3. a. $100.00   **b.** $6.33   **c.** $588.18   **d.** $299.30

4. a. $u_0 = 5000$ and $u_n = \left(1 + \frac{0.05}{4}\right)u_n + 400$ where $n \geq 1$

b. $u_0 = 12500$ and $u_n = \left(1 + \frac{0.075}{12}\right)u_n - 350$ where $n \geq 1$

c. $u_0 = 144500$ and $u_n = \left(1 + \frac{0.062}{12}\right)u_n - 990$ where $n \geq 1$

d. $u_0 = 0$ and $u_n = \left(1 + \frac{0.0375}{12}\right)u_n + 225$ where $n \geq 1$

LESSON 2.1 • Measures of Central Tendency and Box Plots

1. a. Mean: 6.3; median: 7; mode: 7

b. Mean: 6; median: 6.5; mode: 8

c. Mean: 182; median: 180; mode: none

d. Mean: 27.7; median: 32; mode: none

e. Mean: 8; median: 8.8; modes: 5.3, 9.2

f. Mean: 2085; median: 2070; mode: none

2. Sample answers:

a. {11, 12, 13, 14, 25}   **b.** {17, 21, 24, 26, 28, 28}

3. a. 500   **b.** 250   **c.** 500   **d.** 250

e. 750   **f.** 750   **g.** 250

4. a. 2, 3, 6, 9, 10   **b.** 0, 30, 50, 80, 95

c. 1, 2.5, 4, 8, 9   **d.** 16, 36, 52, 60, 70

e. 16.7, 18.65, 20.95, 29.5, 33.9

f. 0.52, 2.20, 4.35, 6.58, 8.15

5. a. B   **b.** C

LESSON 2.2 • Measures of Spread

1. a. $\bar{x} = 18$; deviations: -5.6. 8.3. -8.2, 15.9, -10.4; $s = 11.5$

b. $\bar{x} = 421$; deviations: -186, -8, 84, -310, 279, 205, -64; $s = 208.9$

c. $\bar{x} = 2.1$; deviations: -1.6, 0.5, -0.3, 2.6, -1.2; $s = 1.7$

2. a. $\bar{x} = 41$ in.; $s = 8.9$ in.

b. $\bar{x} = 12.5$ cm; $s = 4.80$ cm

c. $\bar{x} = \$13.80$; $s = \$2.88$

3. a. *median* $= 18$; *range* $= 11$; *IQR* $= 8$

b. *median* $= 7$; *range* $= 11$; *IQR* $= 5$

c. *median* $= 449.5$; *range* $= 766$; *IQR* $= 568$

4. a. 105   **b.** None   **c.** 5, 95

LESSON 2.3 • Histograms and Percentile Ranks

1. a.   **b.**

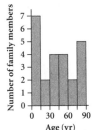

2. a. Bin width: 8; 29 values; bin 16−24

b. Bin width: 12; 72 values; bin 24−36

c. Bin width: 35; 1168 values; bin 140−175

3. a. 73rd percentile   **b.** 54th percentile

c. 44th percentile   **d.** 62nd percentile

LESSON 3.1 • Linear Equations and Arithmetic Sequences

1. a. $u_n = 5 + 8n$ **b.** $u_n = 4.5 + 3.2n$

c. $u_n = 18.25 - 4.75n$ **d.** $u_n = 100n$

2. a. $u_1 = 35$ and $u_n = u_{n-1} - 7$ where $n \geq 2$; common difference: -7; $u_0 = 42$

b. Slope: -7; y-intercept: 42

c. $y = -7x + 42$

3. a. $n = 15$ **b.** $n = 23$

4. a. 3   **b.** -1 **c.** 0.6

d. $-\dfrac{4}{5}$ **e.** 0   **f.** 1

5. a. $y = 11 + 9x$ **b.** $y = -7.5 - 12.5x$

LESSON 3.2 • Revisiting Slope

1. a. 3   **b.** -1 **c.** $-\dfrac{7}{5}$

d. $-\dfrac{5}{3}$ **e.** 0   **f.** Undefined

2. a. 4   **b.** -2.5 **c.** $\dfrac{7}{6}$

d. $-\dfrac{3}{5}$ **e.** -4 **f.** -0.3

3. a. $y = 14$ **b.** $x = -4.8$

   c. $a = 390$ **d.** $b = 6.25$

4. a. $y = 4 + \dfrac{4}{3}x;\ y = -4 - \dfrac{4}{3}x$

   b. $y = 1 - 2x;\ y = 1 + \dfrac{1}{2}x$

5. a. The constants and x-coefficients are negatives of each other. The lines share the same x-intercept.

   b. The equations have the same constant, and the x-coefficients are negative reciprocals of each other. The lines share the same y-intercept and are perpendicular.

LESSON 3.3 • Fitting a Line to Data

1. a. $y = 3 + 2(x - 1)$ **b.** $y = 2 - \dfrac{3}{2}(x + 3)$

2. a. $y = 5 - 3(x - 2)$ **b.** $y = 10 + 0.75(x + 4)$

   c. $y = 2 + 3(x + 4)$ **d.** $y = -5 - 4(x - 2)$

3. a. $u_n = 56$ **b.** $d = -91$

   c. $x = 18$ **d.** $n = 28$

4. a. Sample answer: The points go up to the right. My line has 5 points above the line and 5 points below. They are not concentrated at either end.

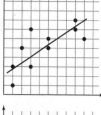

   b. Sample answer: The points go down to the right. My line has 5 points above the line, 5 points below, and 2 points on the line. They are not concentrated, though the 2 points on the line are on the right side.

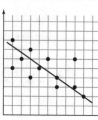

LESSON 3.4 • The Median-Median Line

1. a. 11-11-11   **b.** 15-14-15

   c. 21-22-21   **d.** 19-19-19

2. a. $(8, 8.5)$ **b.** $(3, 4)$

   c. $(15.5, 18.5)$ **d.** $(3.3, 4.4)$

3. a. $y = 8 - 2(x - 5)$, or $y = 2 - 2(x - 8)$

   b. $y = 6 - 1(x + 1)$, or $y = -4 - 1(x - 9)$

   c. $y = -14 + 0.6(x - 20)$, or
   $y = 16 + 0.6(x + 30)$

   d. $y = -22.8 - 3(x - 44.2)$, or
   $y = 34.2 - 3(x - 25.2)$

4. a. $y = 2x + 9$ **b.** $y = -x + 7$

   c. $y = 27.6 + 3.8x$ **d.** $y = 0.8x + 24.4$

LESSON 3.5 • Residuals

1. a. Below   **b.** Above   **c.** Below   **d.** Above

2. a. $-4; -2; 9; 32$ **b.** 15, 25, 39, 74

3. Sample answers are calculated using 1910−2000 as enrollment years.

   a. $\hat{y} = 286.8x - 529{,}431.2$; no, there cannot be a negative number of students enrolled.

   b. $-542.8; 353.2; 1585.2; -1527.0; -4718.0; 2485.2;$ $9985.2; 3218.2; -757.8; 2643.2$

   c. 4349.1 students

   d. In general, the enrollment predicted by the median-median line will be within about 4349 students of the actual value.

   e. 2009−10 enrollment: 7,036.8 students; residual: 72.2

4. a. 2.93   **b.** 4.36

LESSON 3.6 • Linear Systems

1. a. $(0, 2)$ **b.** $(-2, 4)$ **c.** $(5, 6)$

2. Sample answers:

   a. $\begin{cases} 4x + 5y = 40 \\ 4x - 5y = 0 \end{cases}$ **b.** $\begin{cases} 5x - 2y = -31 \\ 2x + 3y = 18 \end{cases}$

   c. $\begin{cases} x + 2y = 24 \\ x - 2y = -18 \end{cases}$

3. a. $y = -4 - 0.5(x - 5)$ **b.** $y = 18 - 4x$

4. a. $x = 1$ **b.** $x = 65$ **c.** $t = 36.6$ **d.** $t = 0.45$

5. a. $(-0.5, 4)$ **b.** $(3, 0.5)$ **c.** $\left(\dfrac{40}{9}, 0\right)$

   d. $(3, 9)$ **e.** $(4.5, -1.5)$ **f.** $(-3, 4.6)$

LESSON 3.7 • Substitution and Elimination

1. a. $s = r - 20$ **b.** $w = \dfrac{8 - z}{2}$, or $w = 4 - \dfrac{1}{2}z$

   c. $y = \dfrac{12 - 3x}{4}$, or $y = -\dfrac{3}{4}x + 3$

   d. $x = \dfrac{8y + 10}{5}$, or $x = \dfrac{8}{5}y + 2$

e. $n = \dfrac{0.2m - 1}{0.5}$, or $n = 0.4m - 2$

f. $y = \dfrac{-250x - 50}{400}$, or $y = -0.625x - 0.125$

2. a. 2   **b.** −3   **c.** 5

3. a. $\left(\dfrac{3}{4}, \dfrac{1}{4}\right)$

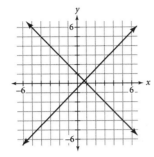

b. (3.6, 2.4)

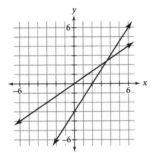

c. $\left(\dfrac{96}{31}, \dfrac{4}{31}\right)$

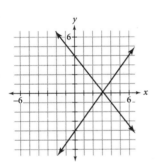

4. a. (−4, −5)   **b.** (−6, 4)   **c.** $\left(\dfrac{2}{5}, -\dfrac{3}{4}\right)$

d. (−20, 10)   **e.** $\left(-\dfrac{1}{2}, \dfrac{2}{5}\right)$ **f.** (0.8, −0.5)

g. (−12, 9)   **h.** (10, −30)   **i.** (−16, 32)

LESSON 4.1 · Interpreting Graphs

1. a. Increasing

  b. Decreasing

  c. Increasing and then decreasing

  d. Decreasing and then increasing

  e. Decreasing

2. a. The child's height at birth

  b. The original loan amount

  c. The height of the top of the building

  d. The family's electric bill for August

  e. The purchase price of the car

3. Possible answers:

  a.   **b.**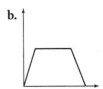

4. a. Independent variable: number of hours worked; dependent variable: money earned. Sample graph:

  b. Independent variable: time; dependent variable: temperature. Sample graph:

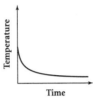

  c. Independent variable: time; dependent variable: speed. Sample graph:

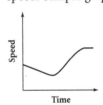

  d. Independent variable: weight of letter in ounces; dependent variable: cost of postage. Sample graph:

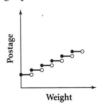

  e. Independent variable: distance from lamp; dependent variable: light intensity. Sample graph:

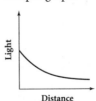

f. Independent variable: time; dependent variable: height. Sample graph:

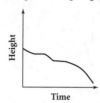

LESSON 4.2 · Function Notation

1. a. Function. Each x-value has only one y-value. Also, no vertical line crosses the graph more than once.

b. Not a function. There are x-values that are paired with two y-values. Also, vertical lines can be drawn that cross the graph more than once.

c. Not a function. There are x-values that are paired with two y-values. Also, vertical lines can be drawn that cross the graph more than once.

2. a. $f\left(-\dfrac{1}{4}\right) = 0$, $f(0) = -1$, $f(0.75) = -2$,
$f(2) = -3$, $f(12) = -7$

b. $f(-3) = -13$, $f(0) = 5$, $f(2) = 7$, $f(5) = -5$, $f(8) = -35$

c. $f(-4) = -\dfrac{1}{4}$, $f(0) = -\dfrac{1}{2}$, $f(5) = 2$,
$f(8) = \dfrac{1}{2}$, $f(24) = \dfrac{1}{10}$

3. a. -10 **b.** -455 **c.** 135
d. 6 **e.** 0.5 **f.** 5
g. -3 **h.** 13 **i.** -8

4. a. If t is the time driven and d is the distance driven, then $d = 65t$

b. If m is the miles driven, d is the number of days the van is rented, and c is the cost of renting the van, then $c = 45d + 0.22m$

LESSON 4.3 · Lines in Motion

1. a. Up 5 units   **b.** Down 3 units
c. Right 2 units   **d.** Left 6 units
e. Left 4 units and down 2 units
f. Right 7 units and up 5 units

2. a. $3(x + 1) = 3x + 3$
b. $-4(x - 2) = -4x + 8$
c. $3 + 2(x + 4) = 2x + 11$
d. $-4 - (x + 3) = -x - 7$
e. $2(x - 5) + 1 = 2x - 9$
f. $3 + 8 - (x + 6) = -x + 5$

3. a. $y = 4 + 2.5x$
b. $y = -1.2(x - 3)$, or $y = -1.2x + 3.6$
c. $y = 5 - (x + 2)$, or $y = 3 - x$
d. $y = -1 + \dfrac{1}{2}(x - 4)$, or $y = -3 + \dfrac{1}{2}x$

4. a. $y = -2 + f(x)$
b. $y = 3 + f(x)$
c. $y = f(x - 3)$
d. $y = -3 + f(x + 2)$

LESSON 4.4 · Translations and the Quadratic Family

1. a. Down 6 units   **b.** Left 5 units
c. Up 2.5 units   **d.** Right 10 units
e. Right 3 units and down 9 units
f. Left 7.5 units and up 2.5 units

2. a. $(0, 0)$ **b.** $(0, 3)$
c. $(0, -4)$ **d.** $(2, 0)$
e. $(-3, 0)$ **f.** $(-1, 5)$
g. $(4, -10)$ **h.** $(7, 4)$
i. $(-5, 8)$

3. a. $y = (x + 3)^2$ **b.** $y = x^2 + 1$

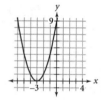 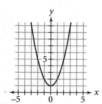

c. $y = (x - 5)^2$ **d.** $y = x^2 - 4$

 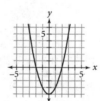

e. $y = (x + 4)^2 + 2$ **f.** $y = (x - 2)^2 - 3$

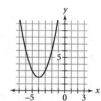 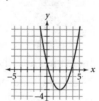

4. a. Translated down 1 unit
b. Translated right 5 units
c. Translated left 3 units
d. Translated up 6 units

Discovering Advanced Algebra More Practice Your Skills
©2004 Key Curriculum Press

5. a. $x = 7$ or $x = -7$ **b.** $x = 5$ or $x = -5$
   c. $x = 8$ or $x = -8$ **d.** $x = 5$ or $x = -13$
   e. $x = 13$ or $x = -7$ **f.** $x = 5$ or $x = -19$
   g. $x = \pm\sqrt{17}$ **h.** $x = \pm\sqrt{30}$
   i. $x = -2 \pm \sqrt{13}$ **j.** $x = 2$ or $x = -10$
   k. $x = -12 \pm \sqrt{21}$ **l.** $x = -5 \pm \sqrt{23}$

LESSON 4.5 · Reflections and the Square Root Family

1. a. Translated left 6 units
   b. Translated up 5 units
   c. Translated down 1 unit
   d. Translated right 8 units

2. a. $y = \sqrt{x + 3}$ **b.** $y = -x^2 + 4$
   c. $y = \sqrt{x} - 4$ **d.** $y = -(x + 2)^2$
   e. $y = \sqrt{-x + 2}$ **f.** $y = -(x - 2)^2 + 3$

3. a. 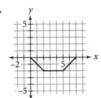   **b.**

   c.

4. a. $Y_1 = \sqrt{x} - 2$, $Y_2 = -\sqrt{x} - 2$; $y = \pm\sqrt{x} - 2$
   b. $Y_1 = \sqrt{x + 2}$, $Y_2 = -\sqrt{x + 2}$; $y = \pm\sqrt{x + 2}$
   c. $Y_1 = \sqrt{x - 6} - 1$; $Y_2 = -\sqrt{x - 6} - 1$;
   $y = \pm\sqrt{x - 6} - 1$

5. a. 7.8 s   **b.** 5.1 s   **c.** 4.3 s

LESSON 4.6 · Stretches and Shrinks and the Absolute-Value Family

1. a. $y = \sqrt{x + 3} - 4$ **b.** $y = -\left|\dfrac{x + 3}{2}\right| + 1$
   c. $y = |x + 3| + 2$ **d.** $y = -(x - 5)^2 + 4$

2. a. Translation right 3 units
   b. Reflection across x-axis
   c. Reflection across y-axis (same as original graph)
   d. Horizontal stretch by a factor of 4
   e. Vertical stretch by a factor of 3
   f. Horizontal shrink by a factor of $\frac{1}{3}$
   g. Reflection across x-axis and translation up 5 units

h. Translation left 2 units and down 1 unit
i. Vertical stretch by a factor of 1.5 and horizontal stretch by a factor of 2
j. Reflection across x-axis and vertical shrink by a factor of 0.5
k. Reflection across x-axis; translation left 4 units and up 6 units
l. Vertical stretch by a factor of 2; translation right 1 unit and down 4 units

3. a. $(3, 0)$ **b.** $(0, 0)$

   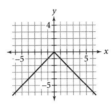

c. $(0, 0)$ **d.** $(0, 0)$

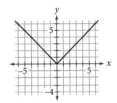   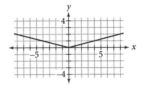

e. $(0, 0)$ **f.** $(0, 0)$

g. $(0, 5)$ **h.** $(-2, -1)$

i. $(0, 0)$ **j.** $(0, 0)$

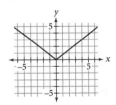   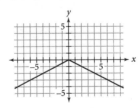

k. $(-4, 6)$ **l.** $(1, -2)$

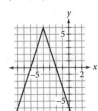   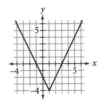

4. a. $x = 9$ or $x = -9$ **b.** $x = 3$ or $x = -7$
   c. $x = 12$ or $x = -2$ **d.** No solution
   e. $x = 9$ or $x = 1$ **f.** $x = 14$ or $x = -14$
5. a. $y = 2\left|\dfrac{x}{4}\right|$ **b.** $y = -4(x + 1)^2 + 2$
   c. $y = -3\sqrt{x} - 4.5$ **d.** $y = 2(x + 1)^2 + 3$
   e. $y = -3\sqrt{x + 2} - 1$ **f.** $y = 3\left|\dfrac{x + 2}{4}\right| + 5$

LESSON 4.7 • Transformations and the Circle Family

1. a. $Y_1 = \sqrt{4 - x^2},\ Y_2 = -\sqrt{4 - x^2}$
   b. $Y_1 = \sqrt{9 - 4x^2},\ Y_2 = -\sqrt{9 - 4x^2}$
   c. $Y_1 = \sqrt{\dfrac{3x - 1}{2}},\ Y_2 = -\sqrt{\dfrac{3x - 1}{2}}$
2. a. $x^2 + y^2 = 4$ **b.** $x^2 + y^2 = 25$
   c. $(x - 2)^2 + y^2 = 1$ **d.** $x^2 + (y + 3)^2 = 9$
   e. $(x + 4)^2 + (y + 1)^2 = 4$
3. a. $-f(x) = -\sqrt{1 - x^2}$
   b. $f(-x) = \sqrt{1 - x^2}$
   c. $2f(x) = 2\sqrt{1 - x^2}$
   d. $f(2x) = \sqrt{1 - (2x)^2} = \sqrt{1 - 4x^2}$
4. a. x-intercepts: $-1, 1$; y-intercepts: $-1, 1$
   b. x-intercepts: $-1, 1$; y-intercept: 1
   c. x-intercepts: $-1, 1$; y-intercept: -1
   d. x-intercepts: $-1, 1$; y-intercept: 3
   e. x-intercepts: $-1, 1$; y-intercept: -2
   f. x-intercepts: $-0.5, 0.5$; y-intercept: 1
   g. x-intercepts: $-0.25, 0.25$; y-intercept: -2
   h. x-intercepts: $-3, 3$; y-intercept: -1
   i. x-intercepts: $-4, 4$; y-intercept: 2
5. a. $(x - 2)^2 + y^2 = 1$; **b.** $x^2 + (y + 4)^2 = 1$;
   circle circle

   c. $x^2 + \left(\dfrac{y}{3}\right)^2 = 1$; **d.** $\left(\dfrac{x}{4}\right)^2 + y^2 = 1$;
   ellipse ellipse

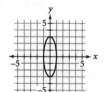 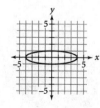

e. $\left(\dfrac{x}{2}\right)^2 + \left(\dfrac{y}{2}\right)^2 = 1$; **f.** $\left(\dfrac{x}{4}\right)^2 + \left(\dfrac{y}{3}\right)^2 = 1$;
   circle ellipse

  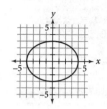

LESSON 4.8 • Compositions of Functions

1. a. $f(-3) = 4$; $f(1) = 2$; $f(5) = 0$
   b. $g(0) = -2$; $g(2) = -2$; $g(4) = -1$
   c. $\{-3, -2, -1, 1, 3, 5\}$
   d. $\{-2, -1, 0\}$
   e. 1
   f. -1
   g. 6
   h. 0
2. a. $-3(x + 2) + 5 = -3x - 1$
   b. $(2x - 2)^2 + 1 = 4x^2 - 8x + 5$
   c. $((x - 1)^2 + 4) + 3 = x^2 - 2x + 8$
   d. -43
   e. 260
   f. 729
   g. -103
   h. 2601
   i. 85
   j. $-3a^2 - 7$
   k. $9a^2 - 30a + 29$
   l. $a^4 + 4a^2 + 4$
3. a. i. $y = (x - 2)^2$
      ii. $f(x) = x^2, g(x) = x - 2$
   b. i. $y = \sqrt{x + 4}$
      ii. $f(x) = \sqrt{x}, g(x) = x + 4$
   c. i. $y = -|x| + 4$
      ii. $f(x) = x + 4, g(x) = -|x|$, or
         $f(x) = -x + 4, g(x) = |x|$
4. a. $f(x) = 1.06x$
   b. $g(x) = 0.15x$
   c. $g(f(x)) = 0.15(1.06x) = 0.159x$
   d. Marla's way: \$7.95; Shamim's way: \$7.50

LESSON 5.1 • Exponential Functions

1. a. $f(3) = 31.25$ **b.** $g(5) \approx 20.1886$
   c. $h(10) \approx 10.6296$ **d.** $h(7) \approx 219.6198$
   e. $r(8) \approx 427.9629$ **f.** $j(10) \approx 21.9282$
   g. $k(20) \approx 3305.0704$ **h.** $q(z) \approx 2515.0376$

2. a. $u_1 = 9.6,\ u_2 = 7.68,\ u_3 = 6.144;\ y = 12(0.8)^x$
   b. $u_1 = 54,\ u_2 = 64.8,\ u_3 = 77.76;\ y = 45(1.2)^x$
   c. $u_1 = 106.05,\ u_2 = 222.705,\ u_3 = 467.6805;$
      $y = 50.5(2.1)^x$
   d. $u_1 = 166.4,\ u_2 = 108.16,\ u_3 = 70.304;$
      $y = 256(0.65)^x$

3. a. $f(0) = 5,\ f(1) = 15,\ f(2) = 45;\ u_0 = 5,\ u_n = 3u_{n-1}$
      where $n \geq 1$
   b. $f(0) = 250,\ f(1) = 125,\ f(2) = 62.5;\ u_0 = 250,$
      $u_n = 0.5u_{n-1}$ where $n \geq 1$
   c. $f(0) = 15.5,\ f(1) = 17.05,\ f(2) = 18.755;$
      $u_0 = 15.5,\ u_n = 1.1u_{n-1}$ where $n \geq 1$
   d. $f(0) = 0.75,\ f(1) = 1.65,\ f(2) = 3.63;\ u_0 = 0.75,$
      $u_n = 2.2u_{n-1}$ where $n \geq 1$
   e. $f(0) = 575,\ f(1) = 46,\ f(2) = 3.68;\ u_0 = 575,$
      $u_n = 0.08u_{n-1}$ where $n \geq 1$
   f. $f(0) = 66,\ f(1) = 66.66,\ f(2) = 67.3266;\ u_0 = 66,$
      $u_n = 1.01u_{n-1}$ where $n \geq 1$

4. a. Decay **b.** Growth **c.** Growth
   d. Decay **e.** Growth **f.** Decay

5. a. 0.75; decrease of 25%
   b. 1.125; increase of 12.5%
   c. 2.25; increase of 125%
   d. $0.8\overline{8}$; decrease of $11.\overline{1}\%$
   e. 0.88; decrease of 12%
   f. 1.6; increase of 60%

6. a. $u_0 = 17500,\ u_n = 0.84u_{n-1}$ where $n \geq 1$
   b.

Year	1	2	3	4	5
Value	$14,700	$12,348	$10,372	$8,713	$7,319

   c. Let x represent the number of years after the car
      was purchased and y represent the value of the
      car. $y = 17500(0.84)^x$

LESSON 5.2 • Properties of Exponents and Power Functions

1. a. $\dfrac{1}{9}$ **b.** $\dfrac{1}{64}$ **c.** $\dfrac{1}{625}$
   d. $\dfrac{1}{25}$ **e.** $\dfrac{1}{343}$ **f.** $\dfrac{1}{1000000}$

g. $-\dfrac{1}{256}$ **h.** $\dfrac{1}{256}$ **i.** $-\dfrac{1}{125}$
j. 32 **k.** $-\dfrac{25}{9}$ **l.** $\dfrac{36}{25}$

2. a. x^{13} **b.** x^7 **c.** x^{-15}
   d. $36x^8$ **e.** $120x^{-11}$ **f.** $-120x^{-20}$
   g. x^{18} **h.** $11x^7$ **i.** $\dfrac{7}{5}x^5$, or $1.4x^5$
   j. x^2 **k.** $125x^{15}$
   l. $-\dfrac{1}{125}x^{18}$, or $-0.008x^{18}$

3. a. $x = -5$ **b.** $x = \dfrac{2}{3}$ **c.** $x = -4$
   d. $x = -7$ **e.** $x = -2$ **f.** $x = \dfrac{4}{3}$

4. a. $x \approx 3.89$ **b.** $x \approx 116.55$ **c.** $x \approx 0.09$
   d. $x \approx 5.62$ **e.** $x \approx 0.39$ **f.** $x \approx 578703.70$
   g. $x \approx 0.91$ **h.** $x = 1.5$ **i.** $x \approx 0.79$

LESSON 5.3 • Rational Exponents and Roots

1. a. Exponential **b.** Neither **c.** Power
   d. Exponential **e.** Power **f.** Neither

2. a. $b^{1/4}$ **b.** $c^{3/2}$ **c.** $d^{7/5}$
   d. $a^{-1/3}$ **e.** $d^{4/3}$ **f.** $r^{-5/2}$

3. a. $x \approx 248832$ **b.** $x \approx 12.90$ **c.** $x = 243$
   d. $x \approx 1.69$ **e.** $x \approx 3.68$ **f.** $x \approx 42.88$
   g. $x = 32$ **h.** $x \approx 18.99$ **i.** $x \approx 58.72$

4. a. $y = x^{3/2} - 3$
   b. $y = -x^{3/2}$
   c. $y = (x + 2)^{3/2}$
   d. $y = 4 + (x - 3)^{3/2}$
   e. $y = 2x^{3/2}$
   f. $y = 0.5(x + 3)^{3/2}$

LESSON 5.4 • Applications of Exponential and Power Equations

1. a. $x \approx 2.63$ **b.** $x \approx 17.58$ **c.** $x \approx 25.88$
   d. $x = 625$ **e.** $x \approx 1.46$ **f.** $x \approx 65.80$
   g. $x \approx 1.66$ **h.** $x \approx 0.05$ **i.** $x \approx 0.03$

2. a. $4x^6$ **b.** $27x^9$ **c.** $7x^{-5}$
   d. $81x^{-12}$ **e.** $1000x^6$ **f.** $-5x^{-5}$
   g. $1296x^{12}$ **h.** $\dfrac{1}{32}x^{-35}$ **i.** $\dfrac{1}{64}x^{36}$

3. a. 5.3% **b.** 7.3% **c.** 3.5%
   d. 3.9% **e.** 4.6% **f.** 7.2%

4. a. Let t represent the year and P represent the
      population. $P = 23000(0.96)^{t-1996}$
   b. 16,592 **c.** 2012

LESSON 5.5 • Building Inverses of Functions

1. a. f: $(-2, -10)$, $(0, -4)$, $\left(\frac{4}{3}, 0\right)$, $(4, 8)$;

    f^{-1}: $(-10, -2)$, $(-4, 0)$, $\left(0, \frac{4}{3}\right)$, $(8, 4)$

b. f: $(-3, -29)$, $(-1, -3)$, $(2, 6)$, $(5, 123)$;
    f^{-1}: $(-29, -3)$, $(-3, -1)$, $(6, 2)$, $(123, 5)$

2. a. 3   **b.** 10.5   **c.** 5   **d.** 4.5

3. a. Function;   **b.** Not a function;
    $y = -\frac{1}{2}x + \frac{5}{2}$ $x = |y|$

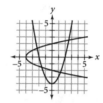 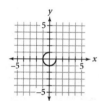

c. Not a function;   **d.** Not a function;
    $y = \pm\sqrt{x + 4}$ $x = -\sqrt{1 - y^2}$

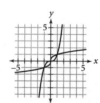 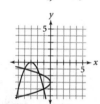

e. Function;   **f.** Not a function;
    $y = x^{1/3}$ $x = -(y + 3)^2$

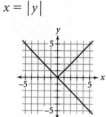

4. a. \$61

b. $p^{-1}(x) = \frac{1}{8}\left(\sqrt{\left(\frac{x - 25}{4}\right)^3} - 3\right)$

c. $15\frac{1}{4}$ person-hours (or 15 person-hours if fractional person-hours are not allowed)

LESSON 5.6 • Logarithmic Functions

1. a. $f^{-1}(x) = \log_5 x$ **b.** $f^{-1}(x) = 2^x$

c. $f^{-1}(x) = 10^x$

2. a. $2^x = 128$; $x = 7$ **b.** $3^x = \frac{1}{81}$; $x = -4$

c. $10^x = 0.001$; $x = -3$ **d.** $12^x = \sqrt[4]{12}$; $x = \frac{1}{4}$

e. $4^x = 32$; $x = \frac{5}{2}$ **f.** $10^x = 1$; $x = 0$

g. $5^x = 125$; $x = 3$ **h.** $8^x = 1$; $x = 0$

i. $20^x = 20$; $x = 1$ **j.** $4^x = \frac{1}{16}$; $x = -2$

k. $9^x = \sqrt[3]{9}$; $x = \frac{1}{3}$ **l.** $10^x = 0.00001$; $x = -5$

3. a. 3   **b.** 4   **c.** 2   **d.** $\frac{1}{2}$

e. -1 **f.** -5 **g.** $\frac{3}{2}$ **h.** $\frac{2}{3}$

i. 9

4. a. $y = 10^x - 3$ **b.** $y = \log(x - 1) + 3$

c. $y = \frac{1}{2}\left(10^{x+2}\right)$

5. a. 1.5850   **b.** 2.9746   **c.** -0.0959 **d.** 2.7712

e. 3.3147   **f.** 3.6789   **g.** 0.5850   **h.** 0.8146

i. 0.7039   **j.** -0.1787 **k.** -0.3117 **l.** -1.0745

LESSON 5.7 • Properties of Logarithms

1. a. $\log \frac{r}{s}$; quotient property of logarithms

b. x^{yz}; power property of exponents

c. a^{-b}; definition of negative exponents

d. $\frac{\log s}{\log r}$; change-of-base property

e. $q^a \cdot q^b$; product property of exponents

f. $m \log_b x$; power property of logarithms

g. $c^m d^m$; power of a product property

h. $\log_b x + \log_b y$; product property of logarithms

i. $\frac{r^m}{s^m}$; power of a quotient property

j. $\sqrt[n]{c^m}$; definition of rational exponents

k. $\log_y x$; change-of-base property

l. $\log_a y^t$; power property of logarithms

2. a. True   **b.** False   **c.** True

d. False   **e.** False   **f.** False

g. True   **h.** True   **i.** True

j. False   **k.** False   **l.** True

3. a. $\log x + \log y + \log z$

b. $\log_2 x + \log_2 y - \log_2 z$

c. $2 \log p - 3 \log q$

d. $\log_5 a + \frac{1}{2} \log b - 4 \log c$

e. $\frac{1}{2} \log_4 r + \frac{1}{3} \log_4 s + \frac{3}{4} \log t$

f. $\frac{1}{3} \log a + \frac{1}{3} \log b + \frac{1}{3} \log c - \frac{1}{4} \log x$

4. a. $x \approx 3.59$ **b.** $x \approx 4.22$ **c.** $x \approx -15.04$

d. $x \approx 16.03$ **e.** $x \approx 83.51$ **f.** $x \approx -24.42$

LESSON 5.8 • Applications of Logarithms

1. a. $x \approx 2.8129$ **b.** $x = 9$ **c.** $x = -6$

d. $x \approx 1.5111$ **e.** $x \approx 11.1144$ **f.** $x \approx 27.9497$

2. a. 14.2 yr   **b.** 11.6 yr   **c.** 13.0 yr

d. 19.3 yr   **e.** 10.4 yr   **f.** 15.4 yr

3. a. 5.0   **b.** 6.3   **c.** $25{,}118{,}864 I_0$

d. $1{,}995{,}262 I_0$

e. The intensity of the 1999 earthquake was about 12.6 times as great as that of the 1998 earthquake.

4. a. 3 months: 372; 6 months: 460; 12 months: 552; 18 months: 608

b. 6 years (72 months)

LESSON 6.1 • Matrix Representations

1. a. $m_{12} = .3$, $m_{21} = .8$ **b.** $r_{11} = .91$, $r_{22} = .27$

c. $t_{11} = .78$, $t_{21} = .32$

2. a.

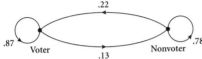

b. $\begin{bmatrix} .87 & .13 \\ .22 & .78 \end{bmatrix}$ **c.** 327

3. a. $(-5, 3)$, $(2, 0)$, $(4, -6)$

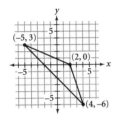

b. $\begin{bmatrix} -8 & -1 & 1 \\ 3 & 0 & -6 \end{bmatrix}$ **c.** $\begin{bmatrix} -1 & 6 & 8 \\ 1 & -2 & -8 \end{bmatrix}$

d. $\begin{bmatrix} 5 & -2 & -4 \\ 3 & 0 & -6 \end{bmatrix}$ **e.** $\begin{bmatrix} -5 & 2 & 4 \\ -3 & 0 & 6 \end{bmatrix}$

f. $\begin{bmatrix} 3 & 0 & -6 \\ -5 & 2 & 4 \end{bmatrix}$

LESSON 6.2 • Matrix Operations

1. a. $x = 12$, $y = 0$, $z = 5$

b. $a = -2$, $b = -5$, $c = 17$, $d = -13$

c. $n_{11} = -19$, $n_{12} = 26$, $n_{21} = 9.5$, $n_{22} = -4$

d. $a = -20$, $b = -12$, $c = 11$, $d = -36$

2. a. $\begin{bmatrix} 0.6 & -4.6 \\ 0.7 & -1.8 \end{bmatrix}$ **b.** $\begin{bmatrix} 18 \\ -22 \\ 4 \end{bmatrix}$

c. Impossible because the dimensions aren't the same.

d. Impossible because the inside dimensions aren't the same.

e. $\begin{bmatrix} 7 \\ 16 \end{bmatrix}$ **f.** $\begin{bmatrix} 40 & -25 \\ -32 & 82 \end{bmatrix}$

3. a.

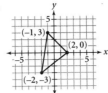

b. $\begin{bmatrix} -3 & 0 & 3 \\ -2 & 2 & -1 \end{bmatrix}$

c.

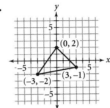

d. Reflection across the line $y = x$

LESSON 6.3 • Row Reduction Method

1. a. $\begin{cases} 3x - y = 5 \\ x + 4y = -2 \end{cases}$ **b.** $\begin{cases} 4x - y + z = 6 \\ -2x + 3y - 2z = 5 \\ 3x + 4y - 4z = 0 \end{cases}$

c. $\begin{cases} 3x - 4y = 2 \\ -x + 3z = 0 \\ -2x + 5y = -1 \end{cases}$

2. a. $\left[\begin{array}{cc|c} 1 & 2 & 8 \\ 2 & -1 & 1 \end{array} \right]$

b. $\left[\begin{array}{ccc|c} 1 & 1 & -1 & 0 \\ 2 & 3 & -3 & -3 \\ -1 & -2 & 2 & 3 \end{array} \right]$

c. $\left[\begin{array}{ccc|c} 2 & 0 & 1 & 8 \\ 0 & 3 & -4 & -1 \\ 4 & -1 & 0 & 3 \end{array} \right]$

3. a. $\left[\begin{array}{cc|c} 4 & -2 & 5 \\ 0 & 1 & -4 \end{array} \right]$

b. $\left[\begin{array}{ccc|c} 1 & 3 & 5 & -2 \\ 0 & -13 & -13 & 6 \\ -2 & 4 & 6 & 1 \end{array} \right]$

c. $\left[\begin{array}{ccc|c} 1 & -3 & 4 & -2 \\ 3 & 1 & -2 & 0 \\ 0 & -1 & 2 & -3 \end{array} \right]$

d. $\left[\begin{array}{ccc|c} -\frac{2}{3} & \frac{1}{6} & -\frac{5}{6} & -2 \\ 4 & -2 & 0 & 4 \\ -12 & -10 & 7 & -80 \end{array} \right]$

4. a. $\begin{cases} m + b + g = 475 \\ 35m + 25b + 15g = 13275 \\ m - b = 45 \end{cases}$

b. $\begin{bmatrix} 1 & 1 & 1 & | & 475 \\ 35 & 25 & 15 & | & 13275 \\ 1 & -1 & 0 & | & 45 \end{bmatrix}$

c. $\begin{bmatrix} 1 & 0 & 0 & | & 220 \\ 0 & 1 & 0 & | & 175 \\ 0 & 0 & 1 & | & 80 \end{bmatrix}$

d. 220 main floor tickets; 175 balcony tickets; 80 gallery tickets

LESSON 6.4 · Solving Systems with Inverse Matrices

1. a. $\begin{cases} 4x - 3y = 5 \\ 2x + 6y = -1 \end{cases}$ **b.** $\begin{cases} 0.5x + 0.8y = 4 \\ 0.1x - 0.2y = 1.5 \end{cases}$

c. $\begin{cases} 2x - 4y = 1 \\ 5x + 3z = 2 \\ 6y - z = 3 \end{cases}$

2. a. $\begin{bmatrix} 4 & -3 \\ 3 & 2 \end{bmatrix}\begin{bmatrix} x \\ y \end{bmatrix} = \begin{bmatrix} 8 \\ -8 \end{bmatrix}$

b. $\begin{bmatrix} 1 & 7 & 1 \\ -5 & -14 & -1 \\ 5 & 1 & -2 \end{bmatrix}\begin{bmatrix} x \\ y \\ z \end{bmatrix} = \begin{bmatrix} -1 \\ -4 \\ 0 \end{bmatrix}$

c. $\begin{bmatrix} 2 & 3 & -1 \\ 3 & 0 & 4 \\ 0 & 1 & -2 \end{bmatrix}\begin{bmatrix} x \\ y \\ z \end{bmatrix} = \begin{bmatrix} -5 \\ -1 \\ -3 \end{bmatrix}$

3. a. Not inverses **b.** Inverses **c.** Inverses

d. Inverses **e.** Not inverses

4. a. $\begin{bmatrix} 2 & 2.5 \\ 1 & 1.5 \end{bmatrix}$ **b.** Inverse does not exist.

c. $\begin{bmatrix} 0.2 & 0.4 & 0.2 \\ -0.4 & 0.2 & -0.4 \\ -0.8 & 0.4 & 0.2 \end{bmatrix}$

5. a. $\begin{cases} 4c + 5d = 146 \\ 6c + 3d = 138 \end{cases}$ **b.** $\begin{bmatrix} 4 & 5 \\ 6 & 3 \end{bmatrix}\begin{bmatrix} c \\ d \end{bmatrix} = \begin{bmatrix} 146 \\ 138 \end{bmatrix}$

c. $\begin{bmatrix} c \\ d \end{bmatrix} = \begin{bmatrix} -\frac{1}{6} & \frac{5}{18} \\ \frac{1}{3} & -\frac{2}{9} \end{bmatrix}\begin{bmatrix} 146 \\ 138 \end{bmatrix}$

d. $[X] = \begin{bmatrix} 14 \\ 18 \end{bmatrix}$

e. CD: \$14; DVD: \$18

LESSON 6.5 · Systems of Linear Inequalities

1. a. $y < 3 - \frac{3}{4}x$ **b.** $y \geq -4 + \frac{4}{5}x$

c. $y < -\frac{9}{8} + \frac{1}{4}x$

2. a. 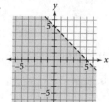 **b.**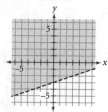

c. 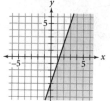 **d.**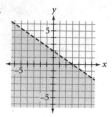

e. 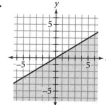 **f.**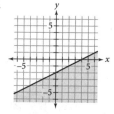

3. a. Vertices: $(0, 0)$, $(7, 0)$, $(3.5, 3.5)$

b. Vertices: $(5, 0)$, $(8, 0)$, $(0, 8)$, $(0, 5)$

  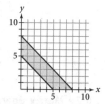

c. Vertices: $(1, 1)$, $(4, 2)$, $(4, 5)$, $(1, 4)$

d. Vertices: $(0, 0)$, $(0, 2)$, $(2, 4)$

 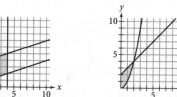

e. Vertices: $(0, 0)$, $(4, 0)$, $(1, 3)$

f. Vertices: $(0, 0)$, $(0, 5)$, $(4, 3)$

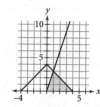

4. a. $1.5a + 1.25h \le 15$ **b.** $2.5m + 10f \le 460$
c. $5c + 8a \ge 83$

LESSON 6.6 · Linear Programming

1. a. $25x + 14y$; maximized
b. $15x + 6y$; maximized
c. $2.75x + 3.25y$; minimized

2. a. $3.5x + 5y \le 21$ **b.** $3x + 4y \le 14$

c. $\begin{cases} 3.5x + 5y \le 21 \\ 3x + 4y \le 14 \\ x \ge 0 \\ y \ge 0 \end{cases}$

d. Vertices: $\left(\dfrac{14}{3}, 0\right)$, $(6, 0)$, $(0, 4.2)$, $(0, 3.5)$

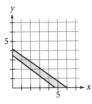

e. $\left(\dfrac{14}{3}, 0\right)$: \$140; $(6, 0)$: \$180; $(0, 4.2)$: \$147; $(0, 3.5)$: \$122.50

f. 6 batches of full sheet cakes, 0 batches of half sheet cakes; \$180

LESSON 7.1 · Polynomial Degree and Finite Differences

1. a. 4   **b.** 5   **c.** 3   **d.** 2
e. 5   **f.** 6

2. a. Polynomial; 3; $-x^3 + x^2 + 1$
b. Polynomial; 4; $0.5x^4 + 0.2x^3 + 0.6x^2$
c. Not a polynomial; $\dfrac{1}{x^2} = x^{-2}$ has a negative exponent
d. Polynomial; 0; already in general form
e. Polynomial; 3; $\dfrac{3}{5}x^3 - \dfrac{2}{3}x^2 + \dfrac{5}{8}x + \dfrac{5}{12}$
f. Not a polynomial; $\sqrt{x} = x^{1/2}$ has a non-integer exponent

3. $D_1 = \{0, -8, -10, -6, 4, 20\}$, $D_2 = \{-8, -2, 4, 10, 16\}$, $D_3 = \{6, 6, 6, 6\}$; degree 3

4. a.

n	1	2	3	4	5	6	7
nth triangular number	1	3	6	10	15	21	28

b. $D_1 = \{2, 3, 4, 5, 6, 7\}$, $D_2 = \{1, 1, 1, 1, 1\}$
c. 2
d. $t(n) = \dfrac{1}{2}n^2 + \dfrac{1}{2}n$, or $t(n) = 0.5n^2 + 0.5n$

LESSON 7.2 · Equivalent Quadratic Forms

1. a. General form
b. Vertex form
c. Factored form and vertex form
d. Factored form
e. Factored form
f. General form and vertex form

2. a. $y = 2x^2 - 10x$ **b.** $y = x^2 - 6x + 9$
c. $y = 1.5x^2 + 6x + 3$ **d.** $y = 2x^2 + 4x - 70$
e. $y = -5x^2 - 5x$ **f.** $y = 3x^2 - 9x - 3.25$
g. $y = -\dfrac{1}{2}x^2 + 6x - 18$ **h.** $y = -x^2 + x + \dfrac{5}{12}$
i. $y = -2.5x^2 - 5x + 60$

3. a. $(0, 0)$ **b.** $(0, 5)$
c. $(4, 0)$ **d.** $(-3, -5)$
e. $(1, 6)$ **f.** $(-6, 10)$
g. $(-4, 6.5)$ **h.** $\left(\dfrac{2}{3}, \dfrac{1}{4}\right)$
i. $\left(-\dfrac{5}{6}, -\dfrac{7}{12}\right)$

4. a. $x = -5$ and $x = 3$ **b.** $x = 1$ and $x = -6$
c. $x = 0$ and $x = 5$ **d.** $x = 7.5$
e. $x = -3.6$ and $x = 4.8$
f. $x = -\dfrac{2}{3}$ and $x = \dfrac{1}{2}$

5. a. $x = 1.5$ **b.** $(-1.5, -5)$; minimum
c. $y = 2(x + 1.5)^2 - 5$

LESSON 7.3 · Completing the Square

1. a. $(x + 5)^2$ **b.** $(x - 11)^2$
c. $\left(x - \dfrac{1}{2}\right)^2$ **d.** $(2x - 5)^2$
e. $(0.2x + 4.5)^2$ **f.** $(3x - 4y)^2$

2. a. 9   **b.** 81   **c.** $\dfrac{25}{4}$, or 6.25
d. $\dfrac{121}{4}$, or 30.25   **e.** 0.16   **f.** 4.6225

3. a. $y = (x - 4)^2 - 2$ **b.** $y = (x + 7)^2 + 1$
c. $y = (x + 2.5)^2 + 1.75$, or $y = \left(x + \dfrac{5}{2}\right)^2 + \dfrac{7}{4}$
d. $y = (x - 5.5)^2 - 2.25$, or $y = \left(x - \dfrac{11}{2}\right)^2 - \dfrac{9}{4}$
e. $y = 5(x - 1)^2 - 8$
f. $y = 2(x + 1.25)^2 - 3.125$

4. a. $(3, 2)$; minimum   **b.** $(-2, -16)$; minimum
c. $(2, 29)$; maximum   **d.** $(-1, 3.5)$; maximum
e. $(-4.5, -30.25)$; minimum
f. $(2.5, 11.125)$; maximum

5. a. $4x^2 + x + 5$; $a = 4$, $b = 1$, $c = 5$

  b. $-5x^2 + 2x$; $a = -5$, $b = 2$, $c = 0$

  c. $3x^2 + 6x + 2$; $a = 3$, $b = 6$, $c = 2$

  d. $-2x^2 + 16x$; $a = -2$, $b = 16$, $c = 0$

  e. $-x^2 + 25$; $a = -1$, $b = 0$, $c = 25$

  f. $2x^2 + 7x - 15$; $a = 2$, $b = 7$, $c = -15$

6. a. $h = -4.9t^2 + 14.7t + 75$

  b. 1.5 s; 86.025 m   **c.** 4.88 s   **d.** 5.69 s

LESSON 7.4 • The Quadratic Formula

1. a. $x = 12$ or $x = -2$ **b.** $x = 1$ or $x = -25$

  c. $x = 3.2$ or $x = -5.8$ **d.** $x = 9.1$ or $x = -3.5$

  e. $x = \dfrac{11}{9}$ or $x = \dfrac{1}{9}$ **f.** $x = -\dfrac{1}{4}$ or $x = -\dfrac{17}{12}$

2. a. 0.742   **b.** 0.293   **c.** 1.693   **d.** -4.436

3. a. $x = -5$ or $x = 2$ **b.** $x = -7$ or $x = -5$

  c. $x = -\dfrac{3}{2}$ or $x = 4$ **d.** $x = \dfrac{-3 \pm \sqrt{29}}{2}$

  e. $x = -\dfrac{1}{3}$ or $x = \dfrac{5}{4}$ **f.** $x = \pm\dfrac{7}{5}$

  g. $x = \dfrac{4 \pm \sqrt{72}}{4} = \dfrac{2 \pm 3\sqrt{2}}{2}$

  h. $x = \dfrac{-7 \pm \sqrt{65}}{8}$

  i. $x = -\dfrac{7}{2}$ or $x = \dfrac{1}{3}$ **j.** $x = 0$ or $x = 5.8$

  k. $x = \pm\sqrt{48} = \pm 4\sqrt{3}$ **l.** $x = 4.8$

4. a. $y = (x - 3)(x - 4)$ **b.** $y = (x + 8)(x - 3)$

  c. $y = (x + 1)(x - 8)$ **d.** $y = 2(x - 3)(x - 1)$

  e. $y = 4(x + 1)(x - 0.5)$

  f. $y = 5(x + 3)(x + 0.8)$

5. a. $y = x^2 - 15x + 54$ **b.** $y = -x^2 - 6x - 8$

  c. $y = 2x^2 + 4x - 70$

  d. $y = \dfrac{1}{2}x^2 - \dfrac{5}{2}x - 12$, or $y = 0.5x^2 - 2.5x - 12$

  e. $y = -x^2 + 13x$

  f. $y = -0.25x^2 + 2.4x - 5.76$

LESSON 7.5 • Complex Numbers

1. a. $10 - 3i$ **b.** $-6 + 7i$

  c. $8 - 20i$ **d.** $-\dfrac{1}{10} + \dfrac{7}{10}i$

  e. $3.5 - 3.8i$ **f.** $4 + 24i$

  g. 13   **h.** $9.4 + 3.6i$

2. a. $3 + 2i$ **b.** $5 + 4i$

  c. -2 **d.** $-7i$

  e. $\dfrac{1}{3} - \dfrac{5}{6}i$ **f.** $-3.25 - 4.82i$

3. a. $\dfrac{3}{5} - \dfrac{1}{5}i$, or $0.6 - 0.2i$ **b.** i, or $0 + i$

  c. $\dfrac{10}{17} + \dfrac{11}{17}i$ **d.** $\dfrac{3}{5} + \dfrac{6}{5}i$, or $0.6 + 1.2i$

  e. $\dfrac{5}{6} - \dfrac{1}{2}i$ **f.** $-\dfrac{7}{13} + \dfrac{22}{13}i$

4. a. $x = 1 \pm 2i$; complex

  b. $x = \dfrac{-1 \pm \sqrt{13}}{2}$; real and complex

  c. $x = \dfrac{1}{2}$ or $x = 1$; real and complex

  d. $x = \pm i\sqrt{7}$; imaginary and complex

  e. $x = -\dfrac{1}{3} \pm i\dfrac{\sqrt{11}}{3}$; complex

  f. $x = \dfrac{5 \pm \sqrt{29}}{2}$; real and complex

  g. $x = \dfrac{-1 \pm i\sqrt{3}}{2}$; complex

  h. $x = \pm\dfrac{3}{2}i$ or $x = \pm 1.5i$; imaginary and complex

  i. $x = \dfrac{-6 \pm \sqrt{140}}{2}$ or $x = -3 \pm \sqrt{35}$; real and complex

5. a. $x^2 - 3x - 28 = 0$ **b.** $x^2 + 121 = 0$

  c. $x^2 + 4x + 13 = 0$

LESSON 7.6 • Factoring Polynomials

1. a. x-intercepts: -6, 5; y-intercept: -30

  b. x-intercept: 8; y-intercept: -64

  c. x-intercepts: -1, 1; y-intercept: -2

  d. x-intercepts: -4, -2; y-intercept: 24

  e. x-intercepts: -2, 1, 6; y-intercept: -12

  f. x-intercepts: 0, 2, -6; y-intercept: 0

2. a. $y = -2(x + 3)(x - 4)$

  b. $y = 0.5(x + 4)(x - 2)$

3. a. $y = x^2 + 2x - 15$

  b. $y = -2x^2 + 12.5$

  c. $y = x^3 + 4x^2 - 5x$

  d. $y = -0.5x^3 - 3x^2 + 4.5x^2$

  e. $y = -x^3 + 144x$

  f. $y = 0.8x^2 - 1.6x - 19.2$

4. a. $2(x - 3)(x + 5)$

  b. $(x - 7)^2$

  c. $x(x - 1)(x - 2)$

  d. $2(x + 2.5)(x - 1)$, or $(2x + 5)(x - 1)$

  e. $(x + 13)(x - 13)$

  f. $(x + 13i)(x - 13i)$

  g. $(x + \sqrt{15})(x - \sqrt{15})$

  h. $(x + i\sqrt{15})(x - i\sqrt{15})$

  i. $(x + 1)(x - 1)(x + 3)(x - 3)$

  j. $12\left(x - \dfrac{3}{4}\right)\left(x + \dfrac{1}{3}\right)$, or $(4x - 3)(3x + 1)$

k. $(x + 1)(x - 3)(x + 7)$

l. $3(x - 1)(x + 4)(x - 2)$

5. Possible graphs:

a.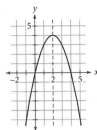

b.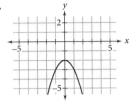

c.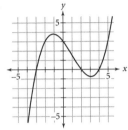

d.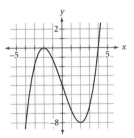

c. $2x^3 - 5x^2 + 8x - 5 = (x - 1)\left(2x^2 - 3x + 5\right)$

d. $6x^3 - 5x^2 + 16x - 8 = (3x - 1)\left(2x^2 - x + 5\right) + (-3)$

4. a. $\pm 1, \pm 2, \pm 4, \pm 8$

b. $\pm 1, \pm 2, \pm 3, \pm 5, \pm 6, \pm 10, \pm 10, \pm 15, \pm 30,$ $\pm\frac{1}{2}, \pm\frac{3}{2}, \pm\frac{5}{2}, \pm\frac{15}{2}$

5. a. $x = -1$, $x = 3$, and $x = 4$; $y = (x + 1)(x - 3)(x - 4)$

b. $x = 5$, $x = 3i$, and $x = -3i$; $y = (x - 5)(x - 3i)(x + 3i)$, or $y = (x - 5)\left(x^2 + 9\right)$

c. $x = -2$, $x = -\frac{4}{3}$, and $x = \frac{1}{2}$; $y = 6(x + 2)\left(x + \frac{4}{3}\right)\left(x - \frac{1}{2}\right)$, or $y = (x + 2)(3x + 4)(2x - 1)$

d. $x = -5$, $x = 5$, $x = 2i$, and $x = -2i$; $y = (x + 5)(x - 5)(x - 2i)(x + 2i)$, or $y = (x + 5)(x - 5)\left(x^2 + 4\right)$

LESSON 7.7 · Higher-Degree Polynomials

1. a. i. $x = -3$, $x = 0$, $x = 2$; ii. $x = -2$, $x = 2$

b. i. 0; ii. 4

c. i. 3; ii. 4

d. i. $y = x(x + 3)(x - 2)$; ii. $y = 0.25(x + 2)^2(x - 2)^2$

2. a. $y = -\frac{1}{2}(x + 4)^2$, or $y = -\frac{1}{2}x^2 - 4x - 8$

b. $y = -x(x - 5)^2$, or $y = -x^3 + 10x^2 - 25x$

c. $y = 2(x - 1)(x - 5)$, or $y = 2x^2 - 12x + 10$

d. $y = -x^2(x - 2)^2$, or $y = -x^4 + 4x^3 - 4x^2$

3. a. $y = 2(x + 3)(x - 5)$; degree 2

b. $y = -(x + 2)^3$; degree 3

c. $y = \frac{1}{2}(x + 2)(x - 1)(x - 3)$, or $y = 0.5(x + 2)(x - 1)(x - 3)$; degree 3

d. $y = -(x - 2i)(x + 2i)(x + 2)^2(x - 5)$, or $y = -\left(x^2 + 4\right)(x + 2)^2(x - 5)$; degree 5

LESSON 7.8 · More About Finding Solutions

1. a. $3x^2 - 2x - 15$ **b.** $x^3 + 4x^2 + 3x + 12$

c. $16x^4 + 8x^3 + 4x^2 + 2x + 1$

2. a. Dividend: $-3x^4 - 5x^3 - 35x + 7$; divisor: $x + 3$

b. 9 -12 36 -3

c. -3 4 -12 1   4

d. Quotient: $-3x^3 + 4x^2 - 12x + 1$; remainder: 4

3. a. $x^2 + 8x - 9 = (x + 9)(x - 1)$

b. $2x^2 - 9x + 2 = (x - 5)(2x + 1) + 7$

LESSON 8.1 · Graphing Parametric Equations

1. a.

t	x	y
-2	3	5
-1	4	2
0	5	1
1	6	2
2	7	5

b.

t	x	y
-4	7	1
-2	5	1
0	3	3
2	1	5
4	1	7

c.

t	x	y
-4	15	12
0	-1	0
2	3	6
4	15	20
8	63	72

2. Possible answers:

a. $(-4, -1)$, $(-1, 1)$, $(2, 3)$, $(5, 5)$

b. $(1, 6)$, $(0, 5)$, $(1, 4)$, $(2, 3)$

c. $(0, 0)$, $(1, 1)$, $(2, 16)$, $(3, 81)$

d. $(2, 0)$, $(3, 0)$, $(6, 2)$, $(11, 6)$

e. $(0, 2)$, $(-1, 1)$, $(-2, -14)$, $(-3, -79)$

f. $(-12, 0)$, $(-5, 1)$, $(-4, 4)$, $(-3, 9)$

3. a. Parabola   **b.** Semicircle

c. Line   **d.** Line

e. Parabola   **f.** Semicircle

4. a.

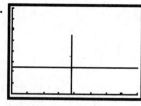

$[0, 800, 100, 0, 800, 100]$

b. 1.6 m/s is Roz's speed, 250 m is the vertical distance between the walkers when they start, 380 m is the horizontal distance between the walkers when they start, and 1.1 m/s is Diana's speed.

c. (380, 250)

d. No; Roz arrives at (380, 250) at 237.5 s and Diana arrives there at 227.3 s.

LESSON 8.2 · Converting from Parametric to Nonparametric Equations

1. a. $t = \dfrac{x+1}{2}$, or $t = \dfrac{1}{2}x + \dfrac{1}{2}$

b. $t = \sqrt[3]{y}$ **c.** $t = \pm\sqrt{x-1}$

d. $t = \pm\sqrt{9 - y^2}$ **e.** $t = -1 \pm \sqrt{y}$

f. $t = \sqrt[3]{5 - x}$

2. a. $y = 3x^2 + 2x - 1$ **b.** $y = \dfrac{x - 11}{2}$

c. $y = \pm 3\sqrt{x} - 2$ **d.** $y = x - 2$

e. $y = -3(x - 2)^2$ **f.** $y = |2x + 1|$

g. $y = \dfrac{2x - 3}{3}$ **h.** $y = \sqrt[3]{4x}$

i. $y = \pm 3\sqrt{2x - 4} - 5$

3. a. $x = 2t - 1$ **b.** $y = t^3 + 1$

c. $y = \left(\dfrac{x+1}{2}\right)^3 + 1$

4.

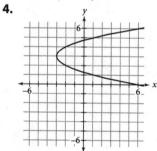

LESSON 8.3 · Right Triangle Trigonometry

1. a. $\sin A = \dfrac{3}{5}$, $\cos A = \dfrac{4}{5}$, $\tan A = \dfrac{3}{4}$; $\sin B = \dfrac{4}{5}$, $\cos B = \dfrac{3}{5}$, $\tan B = \dfrac{4}{3}$

b. $\sin A = \dfrac{12}{13}$, $\cos A = \dfrac{5}{13}$, $\tan A = \dfrac{12}{5}$; $\sin B = \dfrac{5}{13}$, $\cos B = \dfrac{12}{13}$, $\tan B = \dfrac{5}{12}$

2. a. $r \approx 7.6$

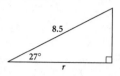

b. $S \approx 42.0°$

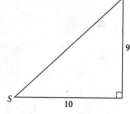

c. $w \approx 10.6$

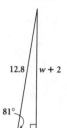

d. $z \approx 7.8$

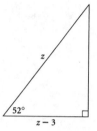

3. a. $\sin 29° = \dfrac{b}{35}$; $b \approx 17$ **b.** $\tan 43° = \dfrac{a}{6.9}$; $a \approx 6.4$

c. $\cos B = \dfrac{5.5}{8.8}$; $B \approx 51°$

4.

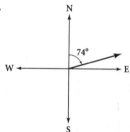

a. 16°   **b.** $x = 375t \cos 16°$, $y = 375t \sin 16°$

c. 901 mi east, 258 mi north

LESSON 8.4 · Using Trigonometry to Set a Course

1. a. 37°; x is positive; y is positive.

b. 53°; x is positive; y is positive.

c. 306°; x is negative; y is positive.

d. 324°; x is negative; y is positive.

e. 222°; x is negative; y is negative.

f. 228°; x is negative; y is negative.

g. 101°; x is positive; y is negative.

h. 169°; x is positive; y is negative.

i. 281°; x is negative; y is positive.

2. a. 78°

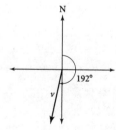

b. 21°

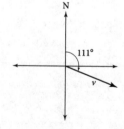

c. 27°   **d.** 66°

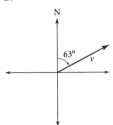   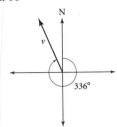

3. a. $x = 15t\cos 42°$, $y = 15t\sin 42°$

b. $x = 32t\cos 63°$, $y = 32t\sin 63°$

c. $x = 12t\cos 32°$, $y = -12t\sin 32°$

d. $x = -21t\cos 33°$, $y = 21t\sin 33°$

e. $x = -39t\cos 25°$, $y = -39t\sin 25°$

4. a. 85.2°; 903 mi   **b.** 276.8°; 755 mi

c. 266.2°; 986 mi   **d.** 94.6°; 1216 mi

LESSON 8.5 • Projectile Motion

1. a. 29 ft   **b.** 7.84 ft   **c.** 72.56 ft

2. a. $t = 0.84$ **b.** $t = 2.04$ **c.** $t = 3.67$

d. $t = 3.11$ **e.** $t = 3.22$ **f.** $t = 3.44$

3. a. $x = 2.3t\cos 0°$, $y = -4.9t^2 + 2.3t\sin 0° + 1.75$, or $x = 2.3t$, $y = -4.9t^2 + 1.75$

b. $x = 132t\cos 28°$, $y = -16t^2 + 132t\sin 28° + 3.5$

c. $x = 128t\cos 42°$, $y = -16t^2 + 128t\sin 42°$

4. a. 0.60 s   **b.** 3.93 s   **c.** 5.35 s

5. a. $x = 6.5t\cos 0°$, $y = -16t^2 + 6.5t\sin 0° + 75$, or $x = 6.5t$, $y = -16t^2 + 75$

b. $-16t^2 + 75 = 0$ **c.** 2.17 s   **d.** 14.11 ft

LESSON 8.6 • The Law of Sines

1. a. $\dfrac{9 \sin 20°}{\sin 75°} \approx 3.2$ **b.** $\dfrac{6.2 \sin 95°}{\sin 45°} \approx 8.7$

c. $\dfrac{12 \sin 120.5°}{\sin 32.4°} \approx 19.3$

2. a. $A = 72.7°$, $b = 7.2$ cm, $a = 7.6$ cm

b. $B = 25°$, $a = 23.8$ mm, $c = 37.1$ mm

3. a. 1   **b.** 1   **c.** 2   **d.** 0

4. a.

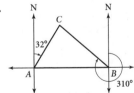

b. $A = 58°$, $B = 40°$, $C = 82°$

c. $\dfrac{\sin 40°}{b} = \dfrac{\sin 82°}{28.0}$; $\dfrac{\sin 58°}{a} = \dfrac{\sin 82°}{28.0}$

d. 18.2 km   **e.** 24.0 km

LESSON 8.7 • The Law of Cosines

1. a. $b \approx 38.5$ **b.** $C \approx 47.5°$

2. a. $a^2 = 9^2 + 12^2 - 2(9)(12)\cos 110°$; $a = \sqrt{225 - 216\cos 110°} \approx 17.3$

b. $5^2 = 3^2 + 4^2 - 2(3)(4)\cos A$; $A = 90°$

c. $c^2 = 3.5^2 + 6.9^2 - 2(3.5)(6.9)\cos 82.5°$; $c = \sqrt{59.86 + 48.3\cos 82.5°} \approx 7.3$

3. a. Law of Sines   **b.** Law of Cosines

c. Law of Cosines   **d.** Law of Sines

4. a. $c = 17.4$ cm, $B = 9.3°$, $A = 22.7°$

b. $A = 30.2°$, $B = 83.6°$, $C = 66.2°$. (The sum of these angle measures is 179.9°, rather than 180°, due to rounding.)

5. a. 29.5 cm   **b.** 88.4°   **c.** 2.6 mi

LESSON 9.1 • Using the Distance Formula

1. a. 13 units   **b.** 25 units

c. 5 units   **d.** $\sqrt{20}$ units, or $2\sqrt{5}$ units

e. $\sqrt{80}$ units, or $4\sqrt{5}$ units

f. $\sqrt{90}$ units, or $3\sqrt{10}$ units

g. $\sqrt{25a^2 + 9}$ units   **h.** $\sqrt{9c^2 + 49d^2}$ units

i. $\sqrt{5}$ units

2. a. $y = -2$ or $y = 14$ **b.** $x = 4 \pm \sqrt{57}$

3. a. $\overline{AB}$; 23.34 units   **b.** $\overline{BC}$; 23.52 units

4. a. $(x + 2)^2 + (y - 3)^2 = 25$

b. $4x + 10y = 29$

c. $x^2 - 6x + y^2 = 27$, or $y = \pm\sqrt{-x^2 + 6x + 27}$

5. a.

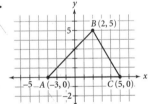

b. Perpendicular bisector of $\overline{AC}$: $x = 1$. Perpendicular bisector of $\overline{AB}$: $x + y = 2$, or $y = -x + 2$. Perpendicular bisector of $\overline{BC}$: $3x - 5y = -2$.

c. $(1, 1)$

d. $DA = \sqrt{17}$ units; $DB = \sqrt{17}$ units; $DC = \sqrt{17}$ units. The three distances are equal.

LESSON 9.2 • Circles and Ellipses

1. a. $(0, 0)$; $r = 4$ **b.** $(3, 0)$; $r = 10$

c. $(0.5, -0.5)$; $r = 0.5$ **d.** $\left(-\dfrac{1}{3}, \dfrac{2}{3}\right)$; $r = \dfrac{5}{7}$

e. $(1, 0)$; $r = 1$ **f.** $(-8, -6)$; $r = 10$

2. a. $(0, 0)$; horizontal: 3; vertical: 5

   b. $(2, 0)$; horizontal: 4; vertical: 2

   c. $(-5, 4)$; horizontal: 3; vertical: 5

   d. $(0, 0)$; horizontal: 7; vertical: 4

   e. $(-3, 0)$; horizontal: 2; vertical: 5

   f. $(0, 6)$; horizontal: 1; vertical: 2

3. a. Major axis: $(0, 5), (0, -5)$;
minor axis: $(3, 0), (-3, 0)$; foci: $(0, 4), (0, -4)$

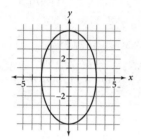

   b. Major axis: $(6, 0), (-2, 0)$; minor axis: $(2, 2)$,
$(2, -2)$; foci: $\left(2 + \sqrt{12}, 0\right), \left(2 - \sqrt{12}, 0\right)$,
or $\left(2 + 2\sqrt{3}, 0\right), \left(2 - 2\sqrt{3}, 0\right)$

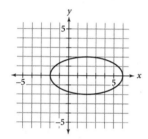

   c. Major axis: $(-5, 9), (-5, -1)$; minor axis:
$(-2, 4), (-8, 4)$; foci: $(-5, 8), (-5, 0)$

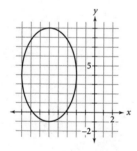

   d. Major axis: $(7, 0), (-7, 0)$; minor axis: $(0, 4)$,
$(0, -4)$; foci: $\left(\sqrt{33}, 0\right), \left(-\sqrt{33}, 0\right)$

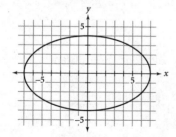

   e. Major axis: $(-3, 5), (-3, -5)$; minor axis:
$(-5, 0), (-1, 0)$; foci: $\left(-3, \sqrt{21}\right), \left(-3, -\sqrt{21}\right)$

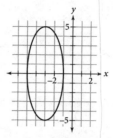

   f. Major axis: $(0, 8), (0, 4)$; minor axis: $(-1, 6)$,
$(1, 6)$; foci: $\left(0, 6 + \sqrt{3}\right), \left(0, 6 - \sqrt{3}\right)$

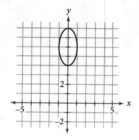

4. a. $x = 11 \cos t, y = 11 \sin t$; circle

   b. $x = \cos t + 5, y = \sin t - 2$; circle

   c. $x = 2 \cos t, y = 4 \sin t$; ellipse

   d. $x = 5 \cos t - 2, y = 5 \sin t + 1$; circle

   e. $x = 7 \cos t + 4, y = 9 \sin t + 6$; ellipse

   f. $x = 8.5 \cos t, y = 10.5 \sin t - 2$; ellipse

5. a. $\left(\dfrac{x}{3}\right)^2 + \left(\dfrac{y}{4}\right)^2 = 1$

   b. $(x - 4)^2 + \left(\dfrac{y - 2}{4}\right)^2 = 1$

   c. $\left(\dfrac{x + 2}{2}\right)^2 + \left(\dfrac{y + 1}{3}\right)^2 = 1$

6. a.

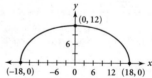

   b. $\left(\dfrac{x}{18}\right)^2 + \left(\dfrac{y}{12}\right)^2 = 1$

   c. Yes; the tunnel is about 11.3 ft high at a distance
of 6 ft from the center. The tunnel is one-way,
so the truck can drive through the center of
the tunnel.

LESSON 9.3 • Parabolas

1. a. $x = -4$ **b.** $(0, 2)$ **c.** $(8.5, 0)$
   d. $(0.5, -3)$ **e.** $y = 9$

2. a. $(0, -5)$; upward; $x = 0$

   b. $(0, 0)$; downward; $x = 0$

   c. $(1, 0)$; right; $y = 0$

   d. $(0, 3)$; left; $y = 3$

   e. $(-1, -2)$; downward; $x = -1$

   f. $(-5, 4)$; right; $y = 4$

3. a. $x = t, y = t^2 + 4$

   b. $x = t^2 - 3, y = t$

   c. $x = t + 2, y = t^2 + 5$

   d. $x = 6t^2 + 5, y = 2t - 3$

   e. $x = t - 3.5, y = 2t^2 - 1.5$

   f. $x = 2t^2 + 4, y = t - 1$

4. a. $(x - 2)^2 = \dfrac{y + 3}{2}$; $x = t + 2, y = 2t^2 - 3$

   b. $(y - 3)^2 = x$; $x = t^2, y = t + 3$

   c. $\dfrac{y - 2}{-\frac{1}{8}} = x^2$; $x = t, y = -\dfrac{1}{8}t^2 + 2$

5. a. 19 ft by 19 ft; 361 ft^2

   b. 5.1 s; 187.6 ft

LESSON 9.4 • Hyperbolas

1. a. $\left(\dfrac{x}{4}\right)^2 - \left(\dfrac{y}{2}\right)^2 = 1$

   b. $\left(\dfrac{y + 3}{2}\right)^2 - \left(\dfrac{x + 1}{2}\right)^2 = 1$

   c. $\left(\dfrac{x}{2}\right)^2 - \left(\dfrac{y}{3}\right)^2 = 1$

   d. $\left(\dfrac{y + 1}{3}\right)^2 - (x - 1)^2 = 1$

2. a. $x = \dfrac{4}{\cos t}, y = 2 \tan t$

   b. $x = 2 \tan t - 1, y = \dfrac{2}{\cos t} - 3$

   c. $x = \dfrac{2}{\cos t}, y = 3 \tan t$

   d. $x = \tan t + 1, y = \dfrac{3}{\cos t} - 1$

3. a. Asymptotes: $y = \pm x$; vertices: $(-1, 0), (1, 0)$;
foci: $\left(\sqrt{2}, 0\right), \left(-\sqrt{2}, 0\right)$

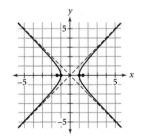

b. Asymptotes: $y = \pm x$; vertices: $(0, -1), (0, 1)$;
foci: $\left(0, \sqrt{2}\right), \left(0, -\sqrt{2}\right)$

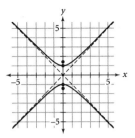

c. Asymptotes: $y = \dfrac{5}{3}x - \dfrac{5}{3}$ and $y = -\dfrac{5}{3}x + \dfrac{5}{3}$;
vertices: $(-2, 0), (4, 0)$; foci: $\left(1 + \sqrt{34}, 0\right)$,
$\left(1 - \sqrt{34}, 0\right)$

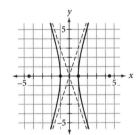

d. Asymptotes: $y = \pm 3x$; vertices: $(-1, 0), (1, 0)$;
foci: $\left(\sqrt{10}, 0\right), \left(-\sqrt{10}, 0\right)$

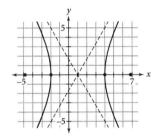

e. Asymptotes: $y = 2x + 7$ and $y = -2x - 5$;
vertices: $(-3, -3), (-3, 5)$; foci: $\left(-3, 1 + \sqrt{20}\right)$,
$\left(-3, 1 - \sqrt{20}\right)$ or $\left(-3, 1 + 2\sqrt{5}\right)$,
$\left(-3, 1 - 2\sqrt{5}\right)$

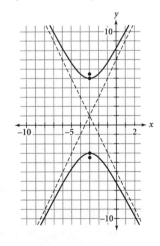

f. Asymptotes: $y = \frac{5}{4}x + 3$ and $y = -\frac{5}{4}x - 7$;
vertices: $(-8, -2)$, $(0, -2)$;
foci: $\left(-4 + \sqrt{41}, -2\right), \left(-4 - \sqrt{41}, -2\right)$

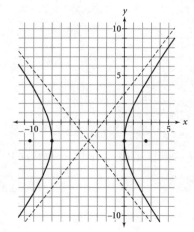

4. a. Hyperbola; $\left(\frac{y}{4}\right)^2 - \left(\frac{x}{3}\right)^2 = 1$

b. Ellipse; $\left(\frac{x}{5}\right)^2 + \left(\frac{y}{3}\right)^2 = 1$

c. Hyperbola; $\left(\frac{x+2}{3}\right)^2 - \left(\frac{y+3}{\sqrt{7}}\right)^2 = 1$

LESSON 9.5 • The General Quadratic

1. a. 16; $(x + 4)^2$ **b.** 121; $(y - 11)^2$

c. $\frac{25}{4}$; $\left(x - \frac{5}{2}\right)^2$

d. $\frac{1}{4}$; $\left(y + \frac{1}{2}\right)^2$

e. 9.61; $(x + 3.1)^2$ **f.** 1.8225; $(y - 1.35)^2$

2. a. Circle; $1x^2 + 0xy + 1y^2 - 14x + 4y + 28 = 0$

b. Parabola; $0x^2 + 0xy + y^2 - 4x + 12y + 56 = 0$

c. Ellipse; $9x^2 + 0xy + 4y^2 - 36x + 24y + 36 = 0$

d. Hyperbola; $16x^2 + 0xy - 9y^2 - 128x + 54y + 31 = 0$

e. Parabola; $0.5x^2 + 0xy + 0y^2 - 4x - 6.5y + 21 = 0$, or $1x^2 + 0xy + 0y^2 - 8x - 13y + 42 = 0$

f. Circle; $1x^2 + 0xy + 1y^2 + 8x - 6y + 0 = 0$

3. a. $x = (y + 3)^2 - 9$ **b.** $\frac{y^2}{4} - \frac{(x-3)^2}{4} = 1$

c. $\frac{(x-4)^2}{4} - \frac{(y-1)^2}{9} = 1$

d. $(x - 6)^2 + (y + 5)^2 = 16$

e. $\frac{(x-1)^2}{25} + \frac{(y+2)^2}{16} = 1$

f. $\frac{y + \frac{7}{2}}{-2} = (x - 1)^2$, or $\frac{y + 3.5}{2} = (x - 1)^2$

4. a. Parabola; $(-3, -9)$ **b.** Hyperbola; $(3, 0)$

c. Hyperbola; $(4, 1)$ **d.** Circle; $(6, -5)$

e. Ellipse; $(1, -2)$

f. Parabola; $\left(1, -\frac{7}{2}\right)$, or $(1, -3.5)$

5. a. $y = \frac{\pm\sqrt{36 - 4x^2}}{3}$, or $y = \frac{\pm 2\sqrt{9 - x^2}}{3}$

b. $y = \frac{\pm\sqrt{x^2 + 2x + 20}}{4}$

c. $y = \frac{5 \pm \sqrt{-48x^2 - 7}}{8}$

d. $y = \frac{-8 \pm \sqrt{-24x^2 + 72x + 76}}{6}$,

or $y = \frac{-4 \pm \sqrt{-6x^2 + 18x + 16}}{3}$

6. a. $(-1, -3)$, $(3, 5)$ **b.** $(2, 1)$, $(1, 4)$

c. $(1, 1)$, $(1, -1)$, $(-1, 1)$, $(-1, -1)$

LESSON 9.6 • Introduction to Rational Functions

1. a. $f(x) = \frac{1}{x + 4}$ **b.** $f(x) = \frac{1}{x + 1} + 6$

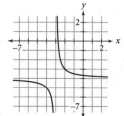
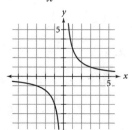

c. $f(x) = \frac{1}{x + 3} - 4$ **d.** $f(x) = \frac{3}{x}$

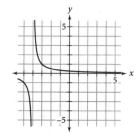
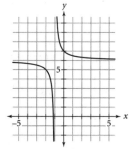

e. $f(x) = \frac{1}{2x} + 1$ **f.** $f(x) = -\frac{1}{x}$

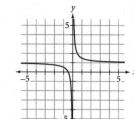
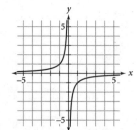

2. a. Horizontal: $y = 0$; vertical: $x = 0$

b. Horizontal: $y = 0$; vertical: $x = -3$

c. Horizontal: $y = -4$; vertical: $x = 0$

d. Horizontal: $y = 0$; vertical: $x = 0$

e. Horizontal: $y = 5$; vertical: $x = 0$

f. Horizontal: $y = -6$; vertical: $x = 2$

g. Horizontal: $y = 2$; vertical: $x = 0$

h. Horizontal: $y = -1$; vertical: $x = -2$

i. Horizontal: $y = 5$; vertical: $x = 4$

3. a. $x = 2$ **b.** $x = \dfrac{13}{6}$ **c.** $x = -\dfrac{13}{2}$

    d. $x = 4$ **e.** $x = -3$ **f.** $x = 2.8$

4. a. $\dfrac{34 + x}{142 + x} = .280$; 8 hits

    b. $\dfrac{78 + x}{120 + x} = 0.75$; 48 mL

LESSON 9.7 • Graphs of Rational Functions

1. a. $\dfrac{(x - 6)(x + 1)}{(x + 5)(x - 5)}$ **b.** $\dfrac{(2x - 1)(x + 2)}{(3x + 1)(x - 2)}$

    c. $\dfrac{(x + 4)(x - 4)}{(2x - 3)(3x + 1)}$ **d.** $\dfrac{x(2x + 5)(2x - 5)}{(x - 6)(x - 8)}$

    e. $\dfrac{x(x + 8)(x - 3)}{(x + 3)(x + 3)}$, or $\dfrac{x(x + 8)(x - 3)}{(x + 3)^2}$

    f. $\dfrac{(3x + 1)(3x - 1)}{x(2x - 3)(x + 1)}$

2. a. $\dfrac{2 + 3x}{x}$ **b.** $\dfrac{x - 1}{x - 2}$ **c.** $\dfrac{6x + 13}{x + 5}$

    d. $\dfrac{x - 7}{2x - 3}$ **e.** $\dfrac{x - 19}{x + 3}$ **f.** $\dfrac{-8x + 27}{3x - 5}$

3. a. Vertical: $x = 1$; horizontal: $y = 1$

    b. Vertical: $x = -3$; horizontal: $y = 2$

    c. Vertical: $x = 0$; horizontal: $y = 0$

    d. Vertical: $x = 2$; horizontal: $y = 0$

    e. Vertical: $x = -2$, $x = 2$; horizontal: $y = 0$

    f. Vertical: $x = -4$, $x = -2$; horizontal: $y = 0$

4. a. Vertical: $x = 1$; slant: $y = x + 1$

    b. Vertical: $x = 0$; slant: $y = x$

    c. Vertical: $x = 1$; slant: $y = x + 2$

    d. Vertical: $x = -3$; slant: $y = 2x - 6$

    e. Vertical: $x = -2$, $x = 2$; slant: $y = x$

    f. Vertical: $x = -2$; slant: $y = -x + 2$

5. a. $(3, -1)$ **b.** $(-5, 1)$ **c.** $(-3, 2)$

    d. $(-2, -4)$ **e.** $(-2, -7)$ **f.** $(-1, 0)$

LESSON 9.8 • Operations with Rational Expressions

1. a. $\dfrac{x(x - 4)}{(x + 3)(x - 4)} = \dfrac{x}{x + 3}$

    b. $\dfrac{(x + 7)(x - 7)}{(x + 7)(x + 7)} = \dfrac{x - 7}{x + 7}$

    c. $\dfrac{2x(x - 5)}{(3x + 4)(x - 5)} = \dfrac{2x}{3x + 4}$

d. $\dfrac{(2x - 1)(2x + 1)}{(3x - 2)(2x + 1)} = \dfrac{2x - 1}{3x - 2}$

e. $\dfrac{(3x - 5)(3x - 5)}{(3x - 5)(3x + 1)} = \dfrac{3x - 5}{3x + 1}$

f. $\dfrac{(4x + 1)(x + 5)}{(5x - 2)(x + 5)} = \dfrac{4x + 1}{5x - 2}$

2. a. $(x + 4)(x + 2)(x - 5)$

    b. $(x + 4)(x - 4)(x + 1)$

    c. $(x - 2)(x - 2)(x - 4)$, or $(x - 2)^2(x - 4)$

    d. $x(x - 8)(x + 1)(2x + 1)$

3. a. $\dfrac{8x + 13}{(x + 2)(x - 1)(x + 1)}$

    b. $\dfrac{-x^2 + 11x - 4}{(x + 7)(x - 7)(x - 1)}$

    c. $\dfrac{x + 5}{(x - 1)(x - 4)}$

    d. $\dfrac{x^3 + 5x^2 - 4x}{(x - 2)(x - 3)(x + 3)}$

    e. $\dfrac{x}{(x - 5)(x - 5)}$, or $\dfrac{x}{(x - 5)^2}$

    f. 1   **g.** $3x$

    h. $\dfrac{36}{(x - 9)(x + 9)}$

4. a. $\dfrac{1}{x(x + 2)}$ **b.** $\dfrac{1}{x + 3}$ **c.** $-\dfrac{1}{2}$

LESSON 10.1 • Defining the Circular Functions

1. a. $\dfrac{\sqrt{3}}{2}$ **b.** $\dfrac{1}{\sqrt{2}}$, or $\dfrac{\sqrt{2}}{2}$ **c.** $\dfrac{1}{2}$

    d. $\dfrac{-1}{\sqrt{2}}$, or $-\dfrac{\sqrt{2}}{2}$ **e.** $-\dfrac{1}{2}$ **f.** $-\dfrac{\sqrt{3}}{2}$

    g. $\dfrac{-1}{\sqrt{2}}$, or $-\dfrac{\sqrt{2}}{2}$ **h.** $-\dfrac{1}{2}$ **i.** $\dfrac{\sqrt{3}}{2}$

    j. 1   **k.** -1 **l.** 0

2. a. 0.6018; 37°   **b.** -0.4226; 65°   **c.** -0.3584; 21°

    d. -0.9659; 15°   **e.** 0.9998°; 89°   **f.** -0.3907; 23°

    g. 0.9816; 11°   **h.** 0.7660°; 50°   **i.** -0.0698; 86°

    j. 0.2079; 78°   **k.** -0.8090; 54°   **l.** -0.9613; 16°

3. a. Periodic; 360°   **b.** Periodic; 4   **c.** Not periodic

4. a. $\theta = 318°$ **b.** $\theta = 55°$ **c.** $\theta = 193°$

    d. $\theta = 194°$ **e.** $\theta = 66°$ **f.** $\theta = 49°$

    g. $\theta = 222°$ **h.** $\theta = 295°$

5. a. $\sin \theta = \dfrac{12}{13}$; $\cos \theta = \dfrac{5}{12}$

    b. $\sin \theta = \dfrac{5}{\sqrt{41}}$, or $\sin \theta = \dfrac{5\sqrt{41}}{41}$;

       $\cos \theta = \dfrac{-4}{\sqrt{41}}$, or $-\dfrac{4\sqrt{41}}{41}$

    c. $\sin \theta = \dfrac{-6}{\sqrt{37}}$, or $-\dfrac{6\sqrt{37}}{37}$;

       $\cos \theta = \dfrac{-1}{\sqrt{37}}$, or $-\dfrac{\sqrt{37}}{37}$

LESSON 10.2 · Radian Measure and Arc Length

1. a. 225°
   b. $\frac{\pi}{12}$
   c. $\frac{11\pi}{6}$

   d. −120°
   e. $-\frac{7\pi}{9}$
   f. $\frac{2\pi}{5}$

   g. −585°
   h. $\frac{13\pi}{3}$
   i. 126°

   j. −330°
   k. 7π
   l. 204°

2. a. 10π
   b. 13.5
   c. $\frac{25\pi}{6}$

   d. $\frac{\pi}{8}$

3. a. $\theta = 120°$
   b. $\theta = 225°$
   c. $\theta = 330°$

   d. $\theta = 270°$
   e. $\theta = \frac{5\pi}{3}$
   f. $\theta = \frac{5\pi}{4}$

   g. $\theta = \frac{7\pi}{6}$
   h. $\theta = \frac{\pi}{6}$

4. a. 427.3 mm
   b. 8.9 mm/min

   c. 0.105 radians/min

LESSON 10.3 · Graphing Trigonometric Functions

1. a. $\frac{2\pi}{3}$
   b. π
   c. $\frac{\pi}{4}$

   d. 4π
   e. 6π
   f. 4π

   g. 3π
   h. $\frac{2\pi}{3}$
   i. $\frac{10\pi}{3}$

2. a. Maximum: 1; minimum: −1; amplitude: 1

   b. Maximum: 1; minimum: −1; amplitude: 1

   c. Maximum: none; minimum: none; amplitude: none

   d. Maximum: 1; minimum: −1; amplitude: 1

   e. Maximum: 3; minimum: 1; amplitude: 1

   f. Maximum: none; minimum: none; amplitude: none

   g. Maximum: 3; minimum: −3; amplitude: 3

   h. Maximum: 0.5; minimum: −0.5; amplitude: 0.5

   i. Maximum: 4; minimum: −1; amplitude: 2.5

3. Possible answers:

   a. $y = -2\sin x$
   b. $y = -4\cos\left(\frac{x}{2}\right)$

   c. $y = -1 + 3\cos(2x)$
   d. $y = -\sin x + 3$

4. a.
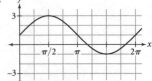

   b.
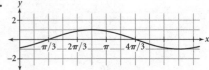

c.
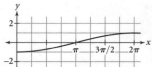

d.
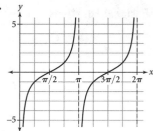

e.
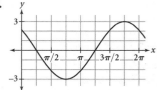

f.

5. a. $y = 2.5\cos\left(x - \frac{\pi}{4}\right)$

   b. $y = 5 + 3\sin\frac{4}{3}x$ or $y = 3\sin\frac{4}{3}x + 5$

LESSON 10.4 · Inverses of Trigonometric Functions

1. a. 36.7°; 0.64
   b. 162.2; 2.83
   c. 91.8°; 1.60

   d. 23.6°; 0.41
   e. 29.9°; 0.52
   f. −42.8°; −0.75

2. a. $\frac{\pi}{3}, \frac{2\pi}{3}, -\frac{4\pi}{3}, -\frac{5\pi}{3}$

   b. $\frac{5\pi}{12}, \frac{19\pi}{12}, -\frac{5\pi}{12}, -\frac{19\pi}{12}$

   c. 1.25, 1.89, −4.39, −5.03

   d. 0.73, 5.55, −0.73, −5.55

   e. $\frac{3\pi}{5}, \frac{7\pi}{5}, -\frac{3\pi}{5}, -\frac{7\pi}{5}$

   f. $\frac{9\pi}{7}, \frac{12\pi}{7}, -\frac{2\pi}{7}, -\frac{5\pi}{7}$

   g. 0.69, 2.45, −3.83, −5.59

   h. 1.07, 5.21, −1.07, −5.21

   i. $-\frac{5\pi}{6}, -\frac{\pi}{6}, \frac{7\pi}{6}, \frac{11\pi}{6}$

3. a. $x = 1.385$ and $x = 1.757$

   b. $x = 0.766$ and $x = 5.517$

c. $x = 2.569$ and $x = -2.569$

d. $x = 1.107$ and $x = 4.249$

4. a. $80.8°$ **b.** $53.9°$ **c.** $25.9°$

LESSON 10.5 • Modeling with Trigonometric Equations

1. a. $x = \left\{\dfrac{\pi}{2}\right\}$ **b.** $x = \left\{\dfrac{2\pi}{3}, \dfrac{4\pi}{3}\right\}$

c. $x = \left\{\dfrac{3\pi}{4}, \dfrac{7\pi}{4}\right\}$ **d.** $x = \left\{\dfrac{\pi}{2}, \dfrac{3\pi}{2}\right\}$

e. $x = \left\{\dfrac{\pi}{9}, \dfrac{5\pi}{9}, \dfrac{7\pi}{9}, \dfrac{11\pi}{9}, \dfrac{13\pi}{9}, \dfrac{17\pi}{9}\right\}$

f. $x = \left\{\dfrac{\pi}{3}, \dfrac{5\pi}{3}\right\}$ **g.** $x = \left\{\dfrac{\pi}{2}, \dfrac{3\pi}{2}\right\}$

h. $x = \left\{\dfrac{\pi}{12}, \dfrac{5\pi}{12}\right\}$ **i.** $x = \left\{\dfrac{3\pi}{2}\right\}$

2. a. $x = \{2.16, 3.38\}$ **b.** $x = \{0.12, 5.36\}$

c. $x = \{1.89, 2.82, 5.03, 5.96\}$

d. $x = \{3.04, 5.71\}$

3. a. 8.5   **b.** 8.5   **c.** 5   **d.** 3.5

e. 13.5   **f.** 5   **g.** $\dfrac{7}{2\pi}$ **h.** 7

i. 4   **j.** 4

4. a. About 14.4 hr (or 14 hr 24 min)

b. Days 105 and 238

c. Summer solstice (day 172) = June 21; day 105 = April 15; day 238 = August 26

LESSON 10.6 • Fundamental Trigonometric Identities

1. a. $\sqrt{3}$ **b.** $-\sqrt{3}$

c. $\sqrt{2}$ **d.** $-\dfrac{2}{\sqrt{3}}$, or $-\dfrac{2\sqrt{3}}{3}$

e. Undefined   **f.** $\dfrac{2}{\sqrt{3}}$, or $\dfrac{2\sqrt{3}}{3}$

g. 1   **h.** $-\dfrac{1}{\sqrt{3}}$, or $-\dfrac{\sqrt{3}}{3}$

i. -2

2. Possible answers:

a. $y = \tan x$ **b.** $y = \sin x$ **c.** $y = \cos x$

d. $y = -\cot x$ **e.** $y = -\sec x$ **f.** $y = -\cot x$

g. $y = -\sin x$ **h.** $y = \sec x$ **i.** $y = -\csc x$

3. a. $\dfrac{\sin \theta + 1}{\cos \theta}$ **b.** $\cos^2 \theta$ or $1 - \sin^2 \theta$

c. 0   **d.** $2 \cos \theta$

e. 1   **f.** $\sin \theta \cos \theta - \sin^2 \theta$

4. a. Not an identity   **b.** Identity

c. Not an identity   **d.** Identity

e. Identity   **f.** Not an identity

g. Identity   **h.** Not an identity

LESSON 10.7 • Combining Trigonometric Functions

1. a. Identity   **b.** Not an identity

c. Not an identity   **d.** Identity

e. Identity   **f.** Not an identity

g. Identity   **h.** Not an identity

2. $\sin 3A = \sin(2A + A) = \sin 2A \cos A + \cos 2A \sin A$

$\qquad = (2 \sin A \cos A)\cos A + (\cos^2 A - \sin^2 A)\sin A$

$\qquad = 2 \sin A \cos^2 A + \cos^2 A \sin A - \sin^3 A$

3. a. $\sin 0.7$ **b.** $\sin 9.6$ **c.** $\cos 2.6$

d. $\sin 10.0$ **e.** $\cos 1.6$ **f.** $\cos(-1.5)$, or $\cos 1.5$

4. a. $\dfrac{\sqrt{2} + \sqrt{6}}{4}$ **b.** $\dfrac{\sqrt{6} + \sqrt{2}}{4}$ **c.** $\dfrac{\sqrt{2} - \sqrt{6}}{4}$

d. $\dfrac{\sqrt{2} - \sqrt{6}}{4}$ **e.** $\dfrac{\sqrt{2} + \sqrt{6}}{4}$ **f.** $\dfrac{\sqrt{6} - \sqrt{2}}{4}$

5. a. $\sin 2x = \dfrac{24}{25}$; $\cos 2x = \dfrac{7}{25}$; $\tan 2x = \dfrac{24}{7}$

b. $\sin 2x = -\dfrac{120}{169}$; $\cos 2x = -\dfrac{119}{169}$; $\tan 2x = \dfrac{120}{119}$

c. $\sin 2x = \dfrac{\sqrt{15}}{8}$; $\cos 2x = \dfrac{7}{8}$; $\tan 2x = \dfrac{\sqrt{15}}{7}$

d. $\sin 2x = -\dfrac{4\sqrt{21}}{25}$; $\cos 2x = -\dfrac{17}{25}$;

$\tan 2x = \dfrac{4\sqrt{21}}{17}$

e. $\sin 2x = -\dfrac{3\sqrt{91}}{50}$; $\cos 2x = -\dfrac{41}{50}$;

$\tan 2x = \dfrac{3\sqrt{91}}{41}$

f. $\sin 2x = -\dfrac{4}{5}$; $\cos 2x = \dfrac{3}{5}$; $\tan 2x = -\dfrac{4}{3}$

LESSON 11.1 • Arithmetic Series

1. a. 5, 11, 17, 23, 29, 35; $d = 6$

b. 7.8, 5.5, 3.2, 0.9, -1.4, -3.7; $d = -2.3$

c. -8.2, -6.4, -4.6, -2.8, -1.0, 0.8; $d = 1.8$

d. 6, -1, -8, -15, -22, -29; $d = -7$

2. a. $-4 + (-3) + (-2) = -9$

b. $1 + 8 + 27 + 64 + 125 = 225$

c. $-4 + (-1) + 2 + 5 = 2$

d. $7 + 13 + 23 + 37 + 55 = 135$

e. $7 + 8.5 + 10 + 11.5 + 13 + 14.5 = 64.5$

f. $5.5 + 17 + 38.5 + 73 = 134$

3. a. 40   **b.** -242.5 **c.** $12\dfrac{3}{4}$, or 12.75

d. 105   **e.** 217   **f.** 8550

g. -366 **h.** 37,350   **i.** 29,925

4. a. 17, 19, 21, 23, 25, 27

   b. $u_1 = 17$ and $u_n = u_{n-1} + 2$ where $n \geq 2$

   c. $u_n = 17 + 2(n - 1)$, or $u_n = 2n + 15$

   d. 41 seats   **e.** 59 seats   **f.** 836 seats

LESSON 11.2 · Infinite Geometric Series

1. a. $0.7 + 0.07 + 0.007 + \cdots$

   b. $u_1 = 0.7$; $r = 0.1$

   c. $S = \dfrac{7}{9}$

2. a. $0.39 + 0.0039 + 0.000039 + \cdots$

   b. $u_1 = 0.39$; $r = 0.01$

   c. $S = \dfrac{13}{33}$

3. a. $0.531 + 0.000531 + 0.000000531 + \cdots$

   b. $u_1 = 0.531$; $r = 0.001$

   c. $S = \dfrac{59}{111}$

4. a. $r = 1.5$; not convergent

   b. $r = \frac{1}{5}$, or 0.2; convergent; $S = \frac{25}{4}$, or 6.25

   c. $r = 0.8$; convergent; $S = 20$

   d. $r = -0.5$; convergent; $S = \frac{20}{3}$, or $6.\overline{6}$

   e. $r = -1.1$; not convergent

   f. $r = 0.1$; convergent; $S = \frac{130}{9}$, or $14.\overline{4}$

5. a. 6   **b.** -12 **c.** 2.2

   d. $\frac{1}{9}$, or $0.\overline{1}$ **e.** 9.6   **f.** $-\frac{25}{11}$, or $-2.\overline{27}$

6. $r = \dfrac{2}{3}$; $1, \dfrac{2}{3}, \dfrac{4}{9}, \dfrac{8}{27}, \dfrac{16}{81}$

7. 10,000

8. $u_1 = 70.4$; $70.4, -42.24, 25.344, -15.2064$

9. About 227 cm

10. 48 m

LESSON 11.3 · Partial Sums of Geometric Series

1. a. $u_1 = 15$, $r = 0.6$, $n = 5$

   b. $u_1 = 4.5$, $r = -0.1$, $n = 6$

   c. $u_1 = 18$, $r = 2.3$, $n = 10$

   d. $u_1 = 30$, $r = 0.5$, $n = 8$

2. a. 0.049152   **b.** $u_7 = 0.768$

   c. 0.12288   **d.** 312.41808

3. a. $u_1 = 5$, $d = 1.2$, $S_{11} = 121$

   b. $u_1 = 150$, $r = -0.2$, $S_9 = 125.000064$

   c. $u_1 = 12.5$, $r = 1.1$, $S_{15} = 397.1560212$

   d. $u_1 = 68.5$, $d = -3.5$, $S_{50} = -862.5$

4. a. 118,096   **b.** 5   **c.** 12   **d.** 0.5

5. a. Geometric; $r = 1.05$ **b.** \$912   **c.** \$49,740

LESSON 12.1 · Randomness and Probability

1. a. .495   **b.** .316   **c.** .572   **d.** .568

2. a. $\dfrac{3}{18} \approx .167$ **b.** $\dfrac{4}{18} \approx .222$

   c. $\dfrac{11}{18} \approx .611$ **d.** $\dfrac{9}{18} \approx .5$

3. a. $\dfrac{65}{100} = .65$ **b.** $\dfrac{4}{6} \approx .667$

LESSON 12.2 · Counting Outcomes and Tree Diagrams

1. $P(a) = .68$, $P(b) = .06$, $P(c) = .94$, $P(d) = .08$,
$P(e) = .92$, $P(f) = .0408$, $P(g) = .2944$

2.

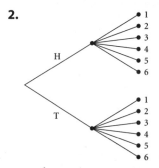

   a. $\dfrac{1}{12} \approx .083$ **b.** $\dfrac{3}{12} = .25$

   c. $\dfrac{5}{12} \approx .417$ **d.** 0

3. a. $\dfrac{169}{2625} \approx .064$ **b.** $\dfrac{16}{2625} \approx .006$

   c. $\dfrac{650}{2625} = \dfrac{26}{105} \approx .248$ **d.** $\dfrac{12}{2625} = \dfrac{4}{875} \approx .005$

4. a. .03   **b.** .315

   c. .45

LESSON 12.3 · Mutually Exclusive Events and Venn Diagrams

1. a. .21   **b.** .66   **c.** 40   **d.** 232

2. a. .18   **b.** .79   **c.** .34   **d.** .05

   e. .66   **f.** .16

3. a.

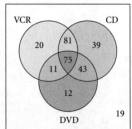

b.

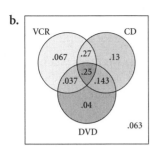

c. .13   **d.** .25

LESSON 12.4 • Random Variables and Expected Value

1. a. Random variable, discrete random variable
   b. Random variable, discrete random variable
   c. Random variable, discrete random variable, geometric random variable
   d. Random variable, discrete random variable
   e. Random variable
   f. Random variable, discrete random variable, geometric random variable

2. a. .35   **b.** .096   **c.** .821

3. a.

x_i	10,000	1,000	100	20	0
$P(x_i)$	.00002	.001	.002	.02	.97698

   b. 48,849   **c.** \$1.80   **d.** Profit; \$10,000

LESSON 12.5 • Permutations and Probability

1. a. 720   **b.** 5040
   c. 6,760,000   **d.** 13,520,000
   e. 60   **f.** 360
   g. 9,000,000   **h.** 112

2. a. 15   **b.** 420
   c. 970,200   **d.** $n(n-1)$, or $n^2 - n$
   e. $(n+1)(n)$, or $n^2 + n$ **f.** 90
   g. 32,760   **h.** 4896
   i. $n(n-1)(n-2)$, or $n^3 - 3n^2 + 2n$
   j. $(n+2)(n+1)(n)$, or $n^3 + 3n^2 + 2n$

3. a. 720 ways   **b.** $\frac{1}{720} \approx .001$
   c. $\frac{1}{6} \approx .167$ **d.** 360 ways
   e. $\frac{4}{6} \approx .667$

LESSON 12.6 • Combinations and Probability

1. a. 10   **b.** 56   **c.** 126   **d.** 1
2. a. 20   **b.** 8   **c.** 2024   **d.** 455
   e. 924   **f.** 20   **g.** 20   **h.** 1
   i. 1   **j.** 1   **k.** 19,701   **l.** 2,704,156

3. a. 35   **b.** 20   **c.** 4845   **d.** 969
   e. 816   **f.** 1848

4. a. 142,506   **b.** $\frac{5}{30} \approx .167$
   c. $\frac{3276}{142506} \approx .023$ **d.** $\frac{792}{142506} \approx .006$
   e. $\frac{23760}{142506} \approx .167$

LESSON 12.7 • The Binomial Theorem and Pascal's Triangle

1. a. $9x^2 - 30xy + 25y^2$ **b.** $16m^2 + 56mn + 49n^2$
   c. $a^3 + 6a^2b + 12ab^2 + 8b^3$
   d. $\frac{1}{8}y^3 - \frac{1}{4}y^2z + \frac{1}{6}yz^2 - \frac{1}{27}z^3$
   e. $r^4 - 4r^3s + 6r^2s^2 - 4rs^3 + s^4$
   f. $16c^4 + 160c^3 + 600c^2 + 1000c + 625$

2. a. $6xy^2$ **b.** $54f^2g^2$
   c. $-10m^2n^3$ **d.** $243b^5$
   e. $67,500c^3d^3$ **f.** $77,520m^{13}n^7$

3. a. $\frac{6}{64} = .09375$ **b.** $\frac{2}{64} = .03125$
   c. $\frac{20}{64} = .3125$ **d.** $\frac{22}{64} = .34375$
   e. $\frac{42}{64} = .65625$

4. a. .668   **b.** .053   **c.** .993
5. a. $\frac{1}{36} \approx .028$ **b.** $\frac{1250}{7776} \approx .161$

LESSON 13.1 • Probability Distributions

1. a. $\frac{10}{18} \approx .556$ **b.** $\frac{3}{18} \approx .167$ **c.** $\frac{6}{18} \approx .333$
   d. $\frac{5}{18} \approx .278$ **e.** $\frac{4.5}{18} = .25$ **f.** $\frac{7}{18} \approx .389$

2. a. $\frac{1}{12}$ **b.** $\frac{3.6}{12} = .3$ **c.** $\frac{2}{12} \approx .167$
   d. 5   **e.** 3.9   **f.** 3.7

3. a. $\frac{1}{8}$ **b.** $mean = median = 5$
   c. No. All x-values from 2 to 8 are equally likely and no other value has a greater probability, so there is no mode.

LESSON 13.2 • Normal Distributions

1. a. $\mu = 32, \sigma \approx 2.5$ **b.** $\mu = 100, \sigma \approx 15$
2. a. $y = \frac{1}{2.5\sqrt{2\pi}} \cdot \sqrt{e^{-((x-32)/2.5)^2}}$
   b. $y = \frac{1}{15\sqrt{2\pi}} \cdot \sqrt{e^{-((x-100)/15)^2}}$

3. a. $\mu = 55, \sigma = 8$ **b.** $\mu = 325, \sigma = 30$
   c. $\mu = 4.8, \sigma = 0.75$ **d.** $\mu = 100, \sigma = 15$

4. a. .4256   **b.** .0458   **c.** .6827   **d.** .4648

e. About 488   f. About 789

g. About 67   h. About 841

LESSON 13.3 • z-Values and Confidence Intervals

1. a. 119   **b.** 86   **c.** 108

   d. 141   **e.** 97   **f.** 130

2. a. 69.4 in.   **b.** 66.1 in.   **c.** 61.7 in.

   d. 68.8 in.   **e.** 59.9 in.   **f.** 57.3 in.

3. a. 99.7%   **b.** 34%   **c.** 47.5%

   d. 95%

4. a. $z = -1.5$ **b.** $z = 2.2$ **c.** .819

5. a. (46.2, 59.0)   **b.** (42.1, 63.1)   **c.** (39.8, 65.4)

   d. (36.1, 69.1)   **e.** (33.4, 71.8)   **f.** (31.5, 73.7)

6. a. (51.3, 53.9)   **b.** (50.5, 54.7)   **c.** (50.0, 55.2)

   d. (49.3, 55.9)   **e.** (48.8, 56.4)   **f.** (48.4, 56.8)

LESSON 13.4 • The Central Limit Theorem

1. a. .3085   **b.** .1587   **c.** .0592   **d.** .0002

2. a. $\bar{x} \leq 92.5$ or $\bar{x} \geq 107.5$

   b. $\bar{x} \leq 30.9$ or $\bar{x} \geq 34.1$

   c. $\bar{x} \leq 244$ or $\bar{x} \geq 256$

   d. $\bar{x} \leq 15.0$ or $\bar{x} \geq 15.6$

3. a. .0228   **b.** .0304   **c.** .1056   **d.** .00003

   e. .0062

LESSON 13.5 • Bivariate Data and Correlation

1.

x	y	$x - \bar{x}$	$y - \bar{y}$	$(x - \bar{x})(y - \bar{y})$
2	5	−5	−6.5	32.5
4	8	−3	−3.5	10.5
6	10	−1	−1.5	1.5
8	13	1	1.5	1.5
10	15	3	3.5	10.5
12	18	5	6.5	32.5

   a. $\bar{x} = 7$, $\bar{y} = 11.5$

   b. 89

   c. $s_x \approx 3.7417$, $s_y \approx 4.7645$

   d. $r \approx .998$

   e. There is a very strong positive correlation in the data.

2. a. Explanatory variable: number of new housing units; response variable: school district enrollment in following year

b. Explanatory variable: dose of medication: response variable: cholesterol levels

3. a. Correlation. The people who take vitamins may take better care of their health, including having healthier diets, exercising more, or receiving better-quality health care.

   b. Correlation. There may be a schedule conflict between the psychology class and the band class so that students cannot enroll in both.

LESSON 13.6 • The Least Squares Line

1. a. 1990   **b.** 14,102   **c.** 7.9057

   d. 1119.4787   **e.** −.9971

2. a. $\hat{y} = 72 + 1.8(x - 20)$, or $\hat{y} = 36 + 1.8x$

   b. $\hat{y} = 6.5 - 4.8(x - 3)$, or $\hat{y} = 20.9 - 4.8x$

   c. $\hat{y} = 8.3 + 0.3528(x - 28.4)$, or

      $\hat{y} = -1.71952 + 0.3528x$

   d. $\hat{y} = 72 - 0.304(x - 1984)$, or

      $\hat{y} = 675.136 - 0.304x$

3. a. −94.52, 113, −6, −65   **b.** 0

   c. 8836, 2704, 12,769, 36, 4225   **d.** 28,570

   e. 84.51

4. a. $\hat{y} = 1.96 + 2.65x$

   b. The slope, 2.65, shows that, according to this model, the percentage of U.S. households with TV that have basic cable service has been increasing by about 2.65% per year. The y-intercept, 1.96, indicates that in 1970 about 1.96% of U.S. households with TV had basic cable service.

   c. 76.16%

   d. There were actually 8.76% fewer households with basic cable service in 1988 than the model predicts. This may be because the percentage increase in cable subscribers has been leveling off in recent years.

LESSON 13.7 • Nonlinear Regression

1. a. $(\log x, \log y)$ **b.** Power

2. a. Exponential; $\hat{y} = 1.089(1.4)^x$

   b. Linear; $\hat{y} = 3.67x + 1.93$

   c. Quadratic; $\hat{y} = 1.286x^2 + 2.286x + 4.6$

3. a. $\hat{y} = 65 - 8.5 \log x$

   b. $\hat{y} = 223.87 \cdot 0.0422^x + 10$

   c. $\hat{y} = 52.8 - 2.3x$

   d. $\hat{y} = 113.24x^{-0.3726} + 10$

Discovering Advanced Algebra More Practice Your Skills

©2004 Key Curriculum Press